Task
MATHS
2

BARBARA BALL & DEREK BALL

Nelson

Thomas Nelson and Sons Ltd
Nelson House Mayfield Road
Walton-on-Thames Surrey
KT12 5PL UK

51 York Place
Edinburgh
EH1 3JD UK

Thomas Nelson (Hong Kong) Ltd
Toppan Building 10/F
22A Westlands Road
Quarry Bay Hong Kong

Thomas Nelson Australia
102 Dodds Street
South Melbourne
Victoria 3205 Australia

Nelson Canada
1120 Birchmount Road
Scarborough Ontario
MIK 5G4 Canada

ISBN 0–17–431164–8
NPN 9 8 7 6 5 4 3 2 1

Printed in Hong Kong.

Acknowledgements

The authors are grateful to all those teachers and students
who have helped by trialling the material in this book.
They value, in particular, the frequent and most helpful
advice they received from Clyde Banks, Sue Pope, Ian
Robinson, Adrian Smith, Philip Whiffing and Trevor Weight.

They would also like to thank teachers and students
at Longslade School, Birstall for their help with some of the
photographs.

ABOUT THIS BOOK

This book is organised into tasks, not into mathematical topics as most mathematics books are. There are twenty-one tasks in this book. While working on any one of these tasks you will meet a number of different mathematical topics

Each task is divided into a number of activities which develop the task. The activities also help to develop your knowledge, skills and understanding of mathematics. Sometimes there are information boxes to explain mathematical words, ideas or techniques.

There are seven sections of review exercises in this book. These exercises contain questions which enable you to consolidate particular mathematical topics. At the end of the book there are five sets of revision exercises.

Throughout this book it is assumed that you have a calculator available whenever you need it (although there are one or two activities to do without a calculator). On many pages there is a picture of a computer. This indicates that a computer, or sometimes a graphical or programmable calculator, would be very useful for working on a particular activity.

Several of the questions in this book are marked with yellow squares. These are somewhat harder than the unmarked questions. Some are marked with blue squares. These are harder still.

At various points in this book you will find a diamond shape in the margin. Inside this diamond shape is a review exercise code and a page number. This tells you that you can turn to the review exercise shown for more practice on the techniques introduced in the task.

CONTENTS

MONTY WRITHES AGAIN

1	2	3	4	5	6	7	8	9	10
2	4	6	8	10	12	14	16	18	20
3	6	9	12	15	18	21	24	27	30
4	8	12	16	20	24	28	32	36	40
5	10	15	20	25	30	35	40	45	50
6	12	18	24	30	36	42	48	54	60
7	14	21	28	35	42	49	56	63	70
8	16	24	32	40	48	56	64	72	80
9	18	27	36	45	54	63	72	81	90
10	20	30	40	50	60	70	80	90	100

You might remember Monty from *Task Maths 1*.

Monty can lie on lots of different number grids.
Here is one of them.

WHAT IS THE GRID AND WHAT IS MONTY?

You could use the computer program *Monty*. The tables grid is a type 2 grid.

I

1	2	3	4	5	6	7	8	9	10
2	4	6	8	10	12	14	16	18	20
3	6	9	12	15	18	21	24	27	30
4	8	12	16	20	24	28	32	36	40
5	10	15	20	25	30	35	40	45	50
6	12	18	24	30	36	42	48	54	60
7	14	21	28	35	42	49	56	63	70
8	16	24	32	40	48	56	64	72	80
9	18	27	36	45	54	63	72	81	90
10	20	30	40	50	60	70	80	90	100

This grid is sometimes called a 'tables grid'.

1 6 × 4 = 24. How does the grid tell you this?

2 The number 24 is on the grid four times. Why is that?

3 What other numbers are on the grid four times?

4 Which numbers are on the grid only once?

5 What is the smallest number which is *not* on the grid? Explain why.

6 You might remember that Monty is a python. He has only one head and only one tail! He always covers seven squares.

Which of these are possible positions for Monty?

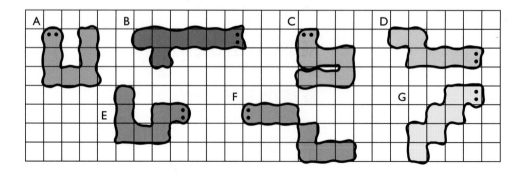

CHOOSY MONTY

You might need tables grids for this activity.

1 Monty is lying on the grid. You add up the numbers in Monty's body.

1	2	3	4	5	6	7	8	9	10
2	4	6	8	10	12	14	16	18	20
3	6	9	12	15	18	21	24	27	30
4	8	12	16	20	24	28	32	36	40
5	10	15	20	25	30	35	40	45	50
6	12	18	24	30	36	42	48	54	60
7	14	21	28	35	42	49	56	63	70
8	16	24	32	40	48	56	64	72	80
9	18	27	36	45	54	63	72	81	90
10	20	30	40	50	60	70	80	90	100

Total = 131

1	2	3	4	5	6	7	8	9	10
2	4	6	8	10	12	14	16	18	20
3	6	9	12	15	18	21	24	27	30
4	8	12	16	20	24	28	32	36	40
5	10	15	20	25	30	35	40	45	50
6	12	18	24	30	36	42	48	54	60
7	14	21	28	35	42	49	56	63	70
8	16	24	32	40	48	56	64	72	80
9	18	27	36	45	54	63	72	81	90
10	20	30	40	50	60	70	80	90	100

Total = 134

(*a*)   What is the smallest total you can get?

(*b*)   What is the largest total you can get?

2 Monty wants to lie *only* on *even* numbers.

(*a*)   What is the smallest total he can lie on?

(*b*)   What is the largest total he can lie on?

(*c*)   Can Monty lie *only* on *odd* numbers?

3 Monty wants to lie *only* on multiples of 3.

1	2	3	4	5	6	7	8	9	10
2	4	6	8	10	12	14	16	18	20
3	6	9	12	15	18	21	24	27	30
4	8	12	16	20	24	28	32	36	40
5	10	15	20	25	30	35	40	45	50
6	12	18	24	30	36	42	48	54	60
7	14	21	28	35	42	49	56	63	70
8	16	24	32	40	48	56	64	72	80
9	18	27	36	45	54	63	72	81	90
10	20	30	40	50	60	70	80	90	100

Total = 84

What is the smallest total he can lie on? What is the largest?

4 What about multiples of 4? Of 5? . . .

SQUARE NUMBERS AND PRIME NUMBERS

You will need tables grids for this activity.

1 Colour in all the square numbers on the tables grid.

What is the largest number of square numbers which can be inside Monty?

2 Colour in all the numbers which are 1 less than square numbers on the tables grid.

3 Colour in all the numbers which are 4 less than square numbers on the tables grid.

4 Colour in all the numbers which are 9 less than square numbers. 16 less. . . .

5 Colour in all the prime numbers on the tables grid. Where are all the prime numbers? Explain why.

STARTING AT 1

You will need tables grids for this activity.

I Here is part of the tables grid. It is a 3 by 3 square containing 1.

1	2	3
2	4	6
3	6	9

There are 9 numbers in the square. The number 9 is also one of the numbers in the square.

The total of the numbers in the square is 36.

The mean of the numbers in the square is $36 \div 9 = 4$.

1 Here is a 2 by 2 square containing 1.

(a) How many numbers are in this square? One of the numbers in the square tells you this. Where is this number in the square?

(b) What is the total of the numbers in this square?

(c) What is the mean of the numbers in this square?

2 Here are two more squares.

1	2	3	4
2	4	6	8
3	6	9	12
4	8	12	16

1	2	3	4	5
2	4	6	8	10
3	6	9	12	15
4	8	12	16	20
5	10	15	20	25

(a) How many numbers are in each of these squares? Where is the number in the square which tells you this?

(b) What is the total of the numbers in each of these squares?

(c) What is the mean of the numbers in each of these squares?

3 Answer question 2 for bigger squares. Try to predict the mean of the numbers in a square.

4 Look at the totals for each square.

What is the total of the numbers in the whole tables grid?

5 Here is a rectangle containing 1.

(a) How many numbers are in this rectangle? Which number in the rectangle tells you this?

(b) What is the total of the numbers in this rectangle?

(c) What is the mean of the numbers in this rectangle?

6 (a) Answer question 5 for rectangles of other sizes.

(b) For which rectangles is the mean a whole number?

I Here is the 3 by 3 square again.

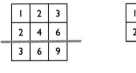

It has been cut into two pieces. The total of the numbers in each piece is the same. So the pieces are 'half' of the square.

7 Here is the 4 by 4 square again.

Show how to cut this square into two pieces so that the total of the numbers in each piece are the same. You won't be able to use a straight cut this time.

8 (a) Try to answer question 7 for squares of other sizes.

(b) Try to answer question 7 for some rectangles.

A1
page
25

9

COLOURING IN THE MULTIPLES

You will need tables grids for this activity.

 Here is the tables grid again. Some of the multiples of 8 have been coloured.

1	2	3	4	5	6	7	8	9	10
2	4	6	8	10	12	14	16	18	20
3	6	9	12	15	18	21	24	27	30
4	8	12	16	20	24	28	32	36	40
5	10	15	20	25	30	35	40	45	50
6	12	18	24	30	36	42	48	54	60
7	14	21	28	35	42	49	56	63	70
8	16	24	32	40	48	56	64	72	80
9	18	27	36	45	54	63	72	81	90
10	20	30	40	50	60	70	80	90	100

1 Look at the picture in the box above. Colour *all* the multiples of 8 on a tables grid.

2 (*a*) Colour all the multiples of 3 on a tables grid.

(*b*) Colour all the multiples of 6 on a tables grid

(*c*) Try colouring other multiples on tables grids.

3 Describe the patterns you obtained in question 2.

Try to explain the different patterns you obtained.

JIGSAW PIECES

See if you can do this activity *without* looking at a tables square.

1 Here is a piece of the tables grid.

Copy this piece and fill in the missing numbers.

2 Here are some more pieces of a tables grid.

(*a*) 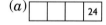 (*b*)   (*c*)   (*d*)   (*e*)

Copy these jigsaw pieces and fill in the missing numbers. In some cases there is more than one answer.

B5 page 46

3 (*a*) What other numbers are like 49 in **2** (*d*)?

(*b*) What other numbers are like 12 and 24 in **2** (*e*)?

TYPE 3 GRIDS

You could use the computer program *Monty* for type 3 grids.

Monty also lies on other types of grid.

Here are some type 3 grids.

147	137	127	117	107	97	87	77	67	57
148	138	128	118	108	98	88	78	68	58
149	139	129	119	109	99	89	79	69	59
150	140	130	120	110	100	90	80	70	60
151	141	131	121	111	101	91	81	71	61
152	142	132	122	112	102	92	82	72	62
153	143	133	123	113	103	93	83	73	63
154	144	134	124	114	104	94	84	74	64
155	145	135	125	115	105	95	85	75	65
156	146	136	126	116	106	96	86	76	66

239	249	259	269	279	289	299	309	319	329
238	248	258	268	278	288	298	308	318	328
237	247	257	267	277	287	297	307	317	327
236	246	256	266	276	286	296	306	316	326
235	345	255	265	275	285	295	305	315	325
234	344	254	264	274	284	294	304	314	324
233	243	253	263	273	283	293	303	313	323
232	242	252	262	272	282	292	302	312	322
231	241	251	261	271	281	291	301	311	321
230	240	250	260	270	280	290	300	310	320

242	241	240	239	238	237	236	235	234	233
232	231	230	229	228	227	226	225	224	223
222	221	220	219	218	217	216	215	214	213
212	211	210	209	208	207	206	205	204	203
202	201	200	199	198	197	196	195	194	193
192	191	190	189	188	187	186	185	184	183
182	181	180	179	178	177	176	175	174	173
172	171	170	169	168	167	166	165	164	163
162	161	160	159	158	157	156	155	154	153
152	151	150	149	148	147	146	145	144	143

1 Here is a type 3 grid.

(a) What is the largest number on this grid?

(b) What is the smallest number on this grid?

(c) What is the number in the square marked * ?

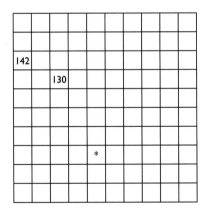

2 Here is another type 3 grid.

(a) What is the largest number on this grid?

(b) What is the smallest number on this grid?

(c) What is the number in the square marked * ?

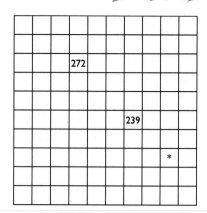

3 Here is another type 3 grid.

(a) What is the largest number on this grid?

(b) What is the smallest number on this grid?

(c) What is the number in the square marked * ?

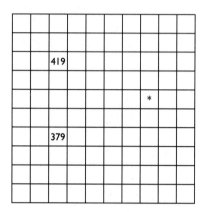

4 Here is another type 3 grid.

(a) What is the largest number on this grid?

(b) What is the smallest number on this grid?

(c) What could the number in the square marked * be?

(d) Why is there more than one answer to question (c) this time?

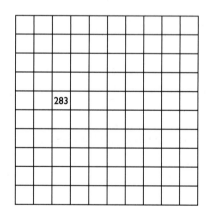

5 Here is another type 3 grid.

(a) What is the largest number on this grid? There are several possible answers.

(b) What is the smallest number on this grid? There are several possible answers.

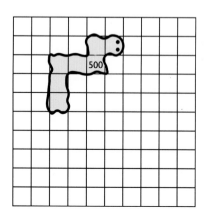

6 Here is Monty lying on another type 3 grid.

(a) What is the largest possible total in Monty?

(b) What is the smallest possible total in Monty?

TYPE 4 GRIDS

Here are some type 4 grids.

28	32	36	40	44	48	52	56	60	64
35	40	45	50	55	60	65	70	75	80
42	48	54	60	66	72	78	84	90	96
49	56	63	70	77	84	91	98	105	112
56	64	72	80	88	96	104	112	120	128
63	72	81	90	99	108	117	126	135	144
70	80	90	100	110	120	130	140	150	160
77	88	99	110	121	132	143	154	165	176
84	96	108	120	132	144	156	168	180	192
91	104	117	130	143	156	169	182	195	208

100	110	120	130	140	150	160	170	180	190
110	121	132	143	154	165	176	187	198	209
120	132	144	156	168	180	192	204	216	228
130	143	156	169	182	195	208	221	234	247
140	154	168	182	196	210	224	238	252	266
150	165	180	195	210	225	240	255	270	285
160	176	192	208	224	240	256	272	288	304
170	187	204	221	238	255	272	289	306	323
180	198	216	234	252	270	288	306	324	342
190	209	228	247	266	285	304	323	342	361

459	476	493	510	527	544	561	578	595	612
486	504	522	540	558	576	594	612	630	648
513	532	551	570	589	608	627	646	665	684
540	560	580	600	620	640	660	680	700	720
567	588	609	630	651	672	693	714	735	756
594	616	638	660	682	704	726	748	770	792
621	644	667	690	713	736	759	782	805	828
648	672	696	720	744	768	792	816	840	864
675	700	725	750	775	800	825	850	875	900
702	728	754	780	806	832	858	884	910	936

Copy these jigsaw pieces and fill in the missing numbers. They are all from type 4 grids.

(a)

(b)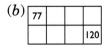

(c)

(d)

(e)

(f)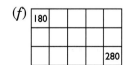

2 POLYGONS AND ANGLES

ANGLES
ROUND A
POINT

You might want to
use ATM MATs
for this activity.

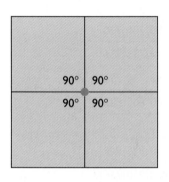

 I The space round a point is divided into 360 degrees.

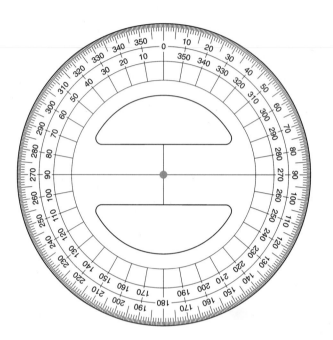

Four squares fit exactly round a point.

So the angle at the corner of a square is 360 ÷ 4 = 90°.

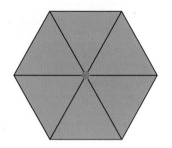

1 (*a*) How many equilateral triangles fit round a point?

(*b*) What is the angle at the corner of an equilateral triangle?

2 (*a*) How many regular hexagons fit together round a point?

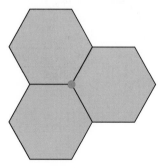

(*b*) What is the angle at the corner of a regular hexagon?

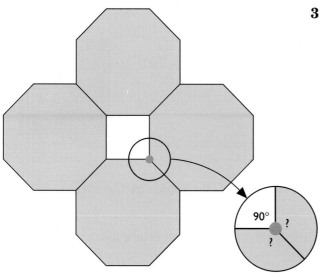

3 This picture shows how four regular octagons fit exactly round a square.

What is the angle at the corner of a regular octagon?

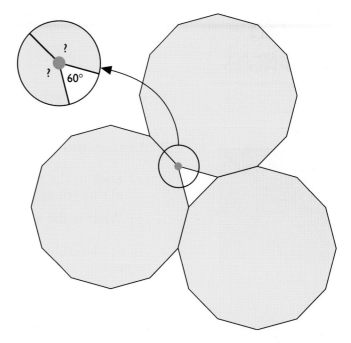

4 This picture shows how three regular dodecagons fit exactly round an equilateral triangle.

What is the angle at the corner of a regular dodecagon?

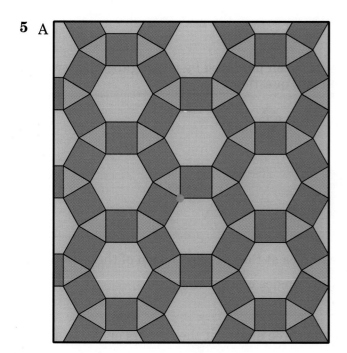

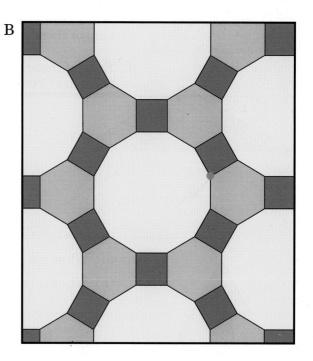

5 A

B

(*a*) Look at picture A above. Write down the size of each of the angles round the red point.

Explain why the shapes fit together exactly round the red point.

(*b*) Now do the same for picture B.

THE SUM OF THE ANGLES OF SQUARES AND TRIANGLES

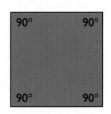

I If you find the sum of the angles at the corners of a square you get $4 \times 90° = 360°$.

90°   90°

90°   90°

1 What do you get if you find the sum of the angles at the corners of an equilateral triangle?

2 A square can be cut in half to get two identical triangles.

(*a*) Look at the red triangle. What are the three angles at the corners of this triangle?

(*b*) What is the sum of the three angles?

3 An equilateral triangle can be cut in half to produce two identical triangles.

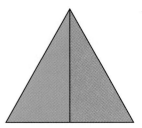

What are the angles at the corners of the grey triangle? What is the sum of these angles?

4 Each of these triangles has been produced by putting together two triangles (from question 2 or question 3).

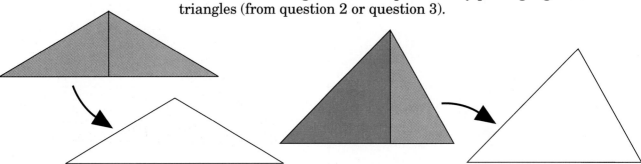

(*a*) What are the three angles at the corners of each of these triangles?

(*b*) What is the sum of the angles of each triangle?

I If you add up the three angles at the corners of *any* triangle you get 180°.

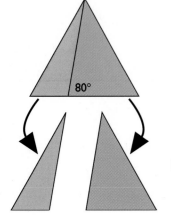

80°

5 Here are two triangles produced by cutting an equilateral triangle into two pieces. The triangle is cut so that an angle of 80° is created. What are the three angles of each of the triangle pieces?

CUTTING QUADRILATERALS TO GET TRIANGLES

You may find the resource sheet '*Shapes*' helpful for this activity.

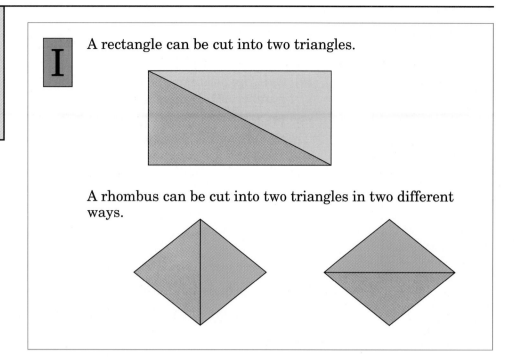

I A rectangle can be cut into two triangles.

A rhombus can be cut into two triangles in two different ways.

1 In how many different ways can each of these quadrilaterals be cut into two triangles?

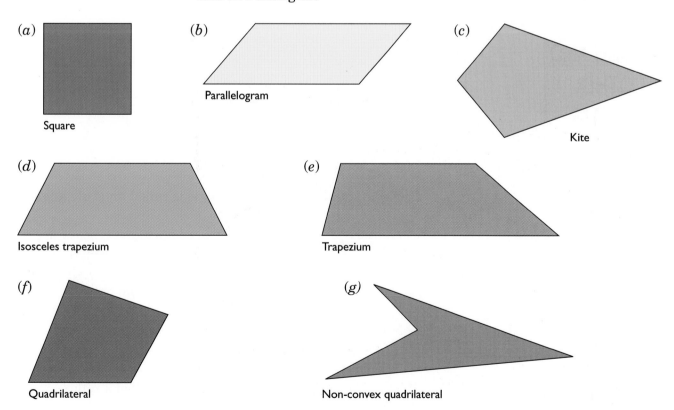

(*a*) Square

(*b*) Parallelogram

(*c*) Kite

(*d*) Isosceles trapezium

(*e*) Trapezium

(*f*) Quadrilateral

(*g*) Non-convex quadrilateral

2 What does *quadrilateral* mean?

3 *Any* quadrilateral can be cut into two triangles. What does that tell you about the sum of the angles at the corners of a quadrilateral?

CUTTING OTHER POLYGONS TO GET TRIANGLES

You may find the resource sheet *Shapes* helpful for this activity.

1 (a) What is the *smallest* number of triangles a pentagon can be cut into? All the cuts must be diagonals.

(b) Can *any* pentagon be cut into this number of triangles?

(c) What is the sum of the angles at the corners of any pentagon?

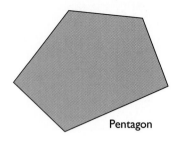
Pentagon

2 (a) What is the smallest number of triangles a hexagon can be cut into?

(b) Can *any* hexagon be cut into this number of triangles?

(c) What is the sum of the angles at the corners of any hexagon?

3 (a) Answer question 2 for a heptagon (7 sides).

(b) Answer question 2 for an octagon (8 sides).

(c) What about 9, 10, 11, 12, 13, ... sides?

(d) What about *N* sides?

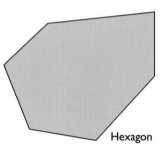
Hexagon

RIGHT ANGLES AND OTHER ANGLES

I   An angle of 90° is called a **right angle**.

Notice the sign people often use to show that an angle is a right angle.

An angle smaller than a right angle is called an acute angle.

acute angle

An angle bigger than a right angle is called an obtuse angle.

obtuse angle

An angle bigger than two right angles is called a reflex angle.

reflex angle

1

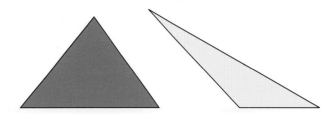

(a) How many acute angles are there in
    (i)   the red triangle?
    (ii) the blue triangle?
    (iii) the yellow triangle?

(b) How many right angles are there in
    (i)   the red triangle?
    (ii) the blue triangle?
    (iii) the yellow triangle?

(c) How many obtuse angles are there in
    (i)   the red triangle?
    (ii) the blue triangle?
    (iii) the yellow triangle?

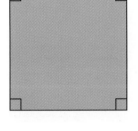

2 Draw some quadrilaterals. Record the numbers of acute angles, obtuse angles and reflex angles in each quadrilateral. See how many different answers you can get.

3 Answer question 2 for pentagons.

4 (a) A square has 4 right angles. Does any other quadrilateral have 4 right angles?

(b) Are there quadrilaterals that have no right angles?

(c) Are there quadrilaterals that have 1 right angle?

(d) Are there quadrilaterals that have 2 right angles?

(e) Are there quadrilaterals that have 3 right angles?

> Draw a picture whenever your answer is yes, in questions 4 and 5.

5 (a) Are there triangles that have no right angles?

(b) Are there triangles that have 1 right angle?

(c) Are there triangles that have 2 right angles?

(d) Are there triangles that have 3 right angles?

> Draw pictures to explain your answers in question 6.

6 What are the possible numbers of right angles for pentagons? For hexagons? For heptagons? . . .

A2
page
25

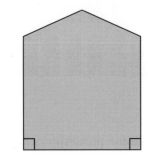

3 TRAINS

Which is the nearest railway station to your school? Do Intercity trains stop at this station? How do you get to London from this station?

For some of the activities in this task you will need a train timetable for your nearest station, and also the prices of tickets to London.

HOW MANY PEOPLE ON A TRAIN?

Above is a photograph of an Intercity 125 train.

I Intercity trains usually have 4 second-class coaches, 2 first-class coaches and a buffet car.

Here is a plan of one of the second-class coaches.

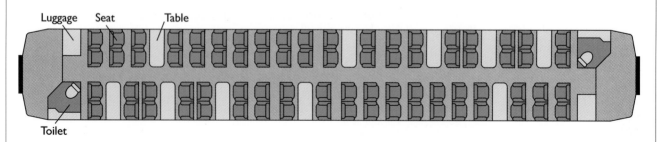

Luggage   Seat   Table

Toilet

1 How many seats are there for passengers in this coach?

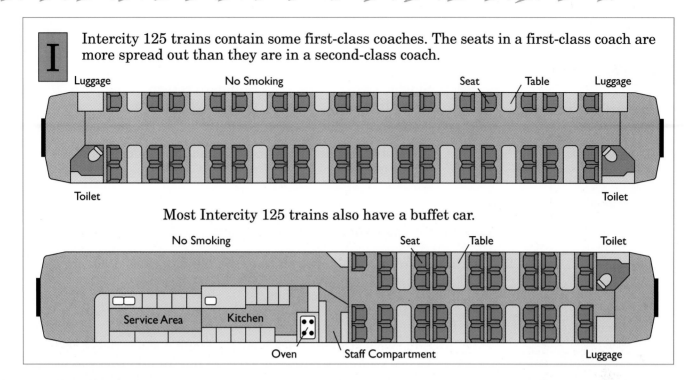

Intercity 125 trains contain some first-class coaches. The seats in a first-class coach are more spread out than they are in a second-class coach.

Luggage No Smoking Seat Table Luggage

Toilet Toilet

Most Intercity 125 trains also have a buffet car.

No Smoking Seat Table Toilet

Service Area Kitchen

Oven Staff Compartment Luggage

2 Are there more seats in a first-class coach or a second-class coach?

3 Estimate the total number of passenger seats on the whole train.

4 In the rush hour this train is sometimes full. All the seats are occupied and there might be about 100 people standing. Estimate the number of people on the train.

5 At a quieter time of the day the train might be half-full. Estimate the number of people on the train.

6 How many people will be on the train if only about 30% of the seats are occupied?

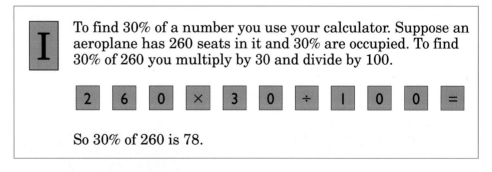

To find 30% of a number you use your calculator. Suppose an aeroplane has 260 seats in it and 30% are occupied. To find 30% of 260 you multiply by 30 and divide by 100.

| 2 | 6 | 0 | × | 3 | 0 | ÷ | 1 | 0 | 0 | = |

So 30% of 260 is 78.

7 About how many people would be on the Intercity train if 80% of the seats were occupied? How many if 65% were occupied?

THE COST OF TRAVEL

If you cannot get ticket prices for your station you can use the resource sheet *'Train information'*.

 You can buy several different types of train ticket:

Single   Standard return
Saver return   Supersaver return
First-class single   First-class return

There are also different prices for adults, children and senior citizens.

1 Find out how much it costs to travel from your nearest station to London. You could find out the costs of different types of ticket.

2 Children's fares are half of adult fares. Senior citizens get a third off adult fares. Find the cost of each of the different types of return ticket for children and for senior citizens.

 Suppose a standard ticket costs £8 and a saver ticket costs £4.50. What percentage of £8 is £4.50? To find this you use a calculator. Divide 4.50 by 8 and multiply by 100.

$4 . 5 0 \div 8 \times 1 0 0 =$

So 4.50 is 56% of 8

3 What percentage of the cost of a first-class ticket is the cost of a standard ticket?

4 What percentage of the cost of a standard return is a saver return?

What percentage is a Supersaver return?

5 Do trains travel directly from your station to London? If so, estimate the total amount paid by all the people on a full London train in the rush hour.

SPECIAL OFFERS

Sometimes British Rail has special offers.

Party Offer!
Travelling in a party? If one adult and at least eight children travel together they can get 65% off the Supersaver price.

Travel On Milk!
BUY AN EXTRA PINT OF MILK FROM YOUR MILKMAN FOR A WEEK. YOU CAN USE THE TOKEN YOU ARE GIVEN TO GET 20% OFF A SUPERSAVER RETURN TO LONDON.

Senior citizens can get 45% off Supersavers on Tuesdays, Wednesdays and Thursdays. Special Midweek Offer!

Summer
Spectacular!

If one adult and at least eight children travel together each child can travel for just £2. The adult pays the Supersaver fare.

From Loughborough the adult Supersaver fare to London is £22.00. This graph shows the total cost to London for one adult and different numbers of children.

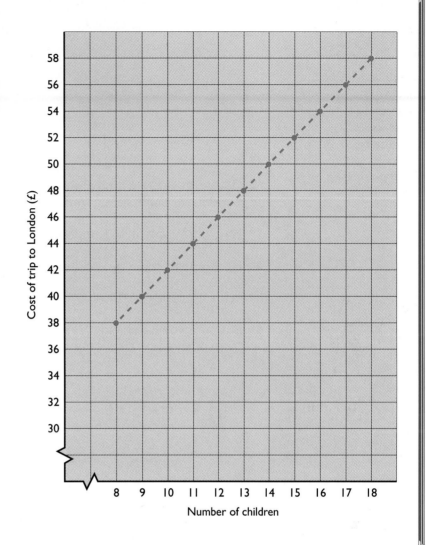

Cost of trip to London (£)

Number of children

1 Find the cost of a Supersaver return to London (or some other large town), if you have a milk token.

2 How much would it cost two senior citizens to travel to London with the midweek offer?

3 (*a*) Draw your own 'Summer Spectacular' graph to London, using the adult fare from your own station.

(*b*) On the same axes draw a graph showing the total cost of the Party Offer, for one adult and different numbers of children.

(*c*) Which of the two offers is better for a group travelling to London? Does it depend on how many children are in the party?

4 Make up some special offers of your own. Ask some questions about your offers. Give them to someone else to answer.

A4
page
27

THE TIMES OF TRAVEL

If you cannot get train times for your local station you can use the resource sheet 'Train information'.

Get a timetable which shows the times of trains from your station to London (or some other town).

1 How many trains to London are there on a weekday?

2 How many trains to London are there on a Sunday?

3 Which journey is slowest? Which journey is fastest?

4 Suppose you catch the first train of the day and come home on the last train of the day. How long will you have in London (or another town)?

> **I** To find the average speed you divide the total distance by the total time. Suppose the total distance is 150 miles and the time of the journey is 87 minutes.
>
> $150 \div 87 = 1.724$
>
> This is the average speed in miles per minute.
> To find the average speed in miles per hour you multiply by 60.
> So the average speed is about 103 mph.

5 Find out the distance from your station to London (or another town). What is the average speed of the fastest train? What is the average speed of the slowest train?

A3 page 26   B7 page 47

THE WEIGHT OF A TRAIN

> **I** An Intercity 125 diesel unit is 70 tonnes. The weight of a passenger coach (when empty) is 33 tonnes.
> (1 tonne = 1000 kg)
>
> The weight of a buffet car is 36 tonnes.

1 Estimate the total weight of an Intercity 125 train when it is empty.

2 Estimate the total weight of an Intercity 125 train when it is full.

C10 page 67

3 When the train is full what percentage of the train's weight comes from passengers?

REVIEW EXERCISES A

EXERCISE 1 Without a Calculator

1 Arrange these numbers in order of size, starting with the smallest.

1010, 990, 909, 99, 1090, 9010, 9009, 999

2 The numbers 46 and 65 can be made using only the digits 2, 3, 7 and 8 and the symbol +.

23 + 23 = 46
27 + 38 = 65

Using only the digits 2, 3, 7 and 8 and the symbol +, make the following:

(a) 64   (b) 66   (c) 54   (d) 155

(e) 105   (f) 69   (g) 99   (h) 132

3 Work out the following:

(a) 3×4 (b) 30×40 (c) 50×60

(d) 7×80 (e) 200×50

4 Work out the following:

(a) 8×50 (b) 8×52 (c) 16×52

(d) 16×104 (e) 32×104

5 You have a calculator on which *only* these keys are working:

Suppose you want to make the number 13. You could make it like this, using 6 key presses:

How would you make each of the following numbers using your broken calculator? Try to use as few key presses as possible for each number. The target is shown after each number.

(a) 9   (4 key presses)

(b) 15   (4 key presses)

(c) 19   (6 key presses)

(d) 42   (6 key presses)

(e) 48   (6 key presses)

(f) 70   (5 key presses)

(g) 105   (6 key presses)

(h) 115   (5 key presses)

(i) 245   (6 key presses)

(j) 364   (5 key presses)

6 Divide the following numbers by 24:

(a) 48   (b) 96   (c) 240

(d) 264   (e) 528   (f) 600

EXERCISE 2 Triangles, Quadrilaterals and Polygons

1

The red shape is an equilateral triangle.

Write down the sizes of its angles.

2

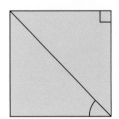

The blue shape is a square.

Write down the sizes of the angles marked.

3 An isosceles triangle is a triangle with two equal angles.

One angle of an isosceles triangle is 80°. What is the size of the other two angles?

(There are two possible answers to this question.)

4

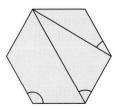

The yellow shape is a regular hexagon. Write down the sizes of the angles marked.

A regular pentagon has all its sides the same length and all its angles the same size.

5 This picture shows a regular pentagon divided into three triangles.

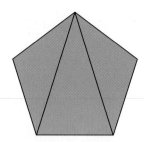

(a) What is the sum of the angles of each triangle?

(b) What is the sum of the angles at the corners of the pentagon?

(c) What is the size of one angle at a corner of the pentagon?

6 This picture shows a regular decagon and two regular pentagons.

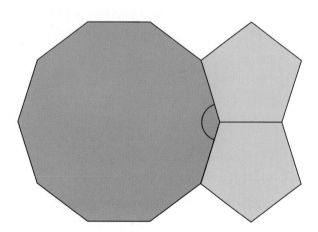

Find the size of the angle marked.

7 (a) Draw a regular hexagon accurately. Draw one diagonal so that one of the pieces is an obtuse-angled triangle. Mark the piece clearly.

(b) Draw a regular hexagon accurately. Draw two diagonals so that one of the pieces is a right-angled triangle. Mark the piece clearly.

(c) Draw a regular hexagon accurately. Draw two diagonals so that one of the pieces is an acute-angled triangle. Mark the piece clearly.

EXERCISE 3 Timetables

1 Here are the times of morning buses on the B route on the island of Guernsey.

TOWN (depart)	7.55	8.45	9.15	9.45	10.15	11.15	12.15
COLBORNE ROAD	8.02	8.52	9.22	9.52	10.22	11.22	12.22
FERMAIN TAVERN	8.04	8.54	9.24	9.54	10.24	11.24	12.24
OLD MILL	8.06	8.56	9.26	9.56	10.26	11.26	12.26
JERBOURG	8.10	9.00	9.30	10.00	10.30	11.30	12.30
OLD MILL	8.15	9.05	9.35	10.05	10.35	11.35	12.35
BELLA LUCE HOTEL	8.17	9.07	9.37	10.07	10.37	11.37	12.37
SAINTS	8.20	9.10	9.40	10.10	10.40	11.40	12.40
ICART CORNER	8.22	9.12	9.42	10.12	10.42	11.42	12.42
VILLETTE HOTEL	8.25	9.15	9.45	10.15	10.45	11.45	12.45
OLD POST	8.30	9.20	9.50	10.20	10.50	11.50	12.50
FERMAIN TAVERN	8.32	9.22	9.52	10.22	10.52	11.52	12.52
COLBORNE ROAD	8.34	9.24	9.54	10.24	10.54	11.54	12.54
TOWN (arrival)	8.40	9.30	10.00	10.30	11.00	12.00	13.00

(a) A bus leaves Jerbourg at 10.30 a.m. At what time does it get to Villette Hotel?

(b) Jane wants to travel from Bella Luce Hotel to Town. What is the earliest time she can arrive in Town?

(c) Gareth is going from Colborne Road to Saints. He wants to arrive at Saints before quarter past ten. What is the latest bus he can catch from Colborne Road?

(d) How long does the bus take from Jerbourg to Town?

(e) How long does the bus take from Town to Jerbourg?

2 Here is part of the timetable for trains from South Yorkshire and the East Midlands to London on Sundays.

Leeds **10**	d	—	—	—	—	0930	—	1130	—	—
Wakefield Westgate **7**	d	—	—	—	—	0947	—	1147	—	—
Sheffield **7**	d	—	—	0840	—	1040	—	1240	—	1340
Chesterfield	d	—	—	0908	—	1108	—	1308	—	1408
Derby **10**	d	0730	—	0932	—	1132	—	1332	—	1432
Long Eaton	d	—	—	—	—	—	—	—	—	—
Alfreton & Mansfield Parkway	d	—	—	—	—	—	—	—	—	—
Nottingham **8**	d	—	0825	—	1023	—	1223	—	1405	—
Beeston	d	—	—	—	—	—	—	—	—	—
Loughborough	d	—	0848	—	1048	—	1246	1357	—	1457
Leicester **10**	d	0812	0912	1016	1112	1216	1310	1421	1447	1521
Market Harborough	d	0826	0926	—	1126	—	1324	—	1501	—
Kettering	d	0836	0936	—	1136	—	1334	—	1509	—
Wellingborough	d	0844	0944	—	1144	—	1342	—	1517	—
Bedford	a	0902	1002	—	1202	—	1402	—	1537	—
Luton	a	0920	1020	1110	—	1310	—	1515	—	1615
London St. Pancras	a	0958	1056	1146	1253	1346	1453	1551	1628	1645

(a) A train leaves Leeds at 9.30 a.m. At what time does it arrive in London?

(b) Sidhartha travels from Chesterfield to Luton. He catches a train from Chesterfield at eight minutes past nine. At what time does he arrive at Luton?

(c) How many of the trains listed in the timetable stop at Loughborough?

(d) How long does the journey from Loughborough to London take on the train which leaves Loughborough at 10.48 a.m.?

(e) How long does the journey from Leicester to London take on the train which leaves Leicester at 2.47 p.m.?

(f) Which is the quickest train from Derby to Leicester? Which is the slowest?

EXERCISE 4 Money and Percentages

1

Fish Bar

Cod	£1.25 per portion
Place	£1.35 per portion
Chips	70p per portion
Sausage	50p each
Coke	32p
Lemonade	27p

(a) Emily buys two sausages and a portion of chips. How much does she pay?

(b) Drew buys a portion of cod, a portion of chips and a can of coke. He pays with a five pound note. How much change does he get?

(c) Two of the people in Jenny's family want cod, two want plaice and they all want chips. Jenny pays with a ten pound note. How much change does she get?

(d) Alex is buying food for herself and her mother. Her mother wants plaice and chips. Alex decides she would like as many sausages as possible with her portion of chips. The only money she has is a five pound note.

How many sausages does she buy?

2 Gurpaul delivers newspapers. He earns a basic wage of £3 plus 2p for every paper he delivers.

(a) One week he delivered 50 papers. How much money did he earn?

(b) Another week he earned £4.68. How many papers did he deliver?

3 Three friends agree to give 10% of their pocket money one week to Oxfam.

James gets £4 pocket money each week, Ed gets £6 each week and Emma gets £7.50. How much does each pay to Oxfam?

4

How much does the coat cost?

5

Simon buys three pairs of shoes in the sale. How much does he pay?

6 There are 24 students in a class. 6 of them wear glasses. 15 of them are girls.

(a) What percentage wear glasses?

(b) What percentage do not wear glasses?

(c) What percentage are girls?

(d) What percentage are boys?

4 CUBOIDS

BUILDING CUBOIDS

 Without counting, take a large handful of interlocking cubes. Now count the cubes. How many cubes do you have?

Suppose you have picked 16 cubes. Here are two of the cuboids you could make.

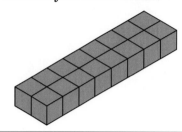 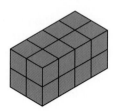

1 How many different cuboids can you make using your cubes? You must use *all* the cubes for each cuboid. Keep a record of all the cuboids you can make.

 You could use *Spread* for this activity.

Choose to have 4 columns.
Enter this formula into column D.
   D = A * B * C
Enter the edge lengths of each cuboid
   into columns A, B and C.
Press U to update the table.

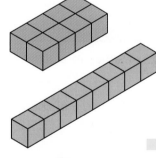

2 Now try a different number of cubes. How many cuboids can you make using this number?

3 Find a way of predicting how many cuboids you can make using a given number of cubes.

4 Can you make more cuboids using 36 cubes or using 37 cubes?

5 How many cuboids can you make using exactly 100 cubes?

6 How many cuboids can be made using exactly a million cubes?

7 Figure 1 shows all the possible cuboids using 8 cubes.

(*a*) What is the surface area of each of these three cuboids?

(*b*) Find the surface areas of all cuboids using 12 cubes. Which cuboid has the biggest surface area? Which cuboid has the smallest surface area?

(*c*) Choose a different number of cubes. Find the surface areas of all cuboids using this number of cubes. Which cuboid has the biggest surface area? Which cuboid has the smallest surface area?

Figure 1

C9 page 66

PRIME FACTORS

 Are you surprised that you can make more cuboids with 12 cubes than you can with 13 cubes? You can make more cuboids with 12 cubes, because 12 has more factors.

One way of looking at this problem is to write numbers as the product of prime factors.

For example:

$6 = 2 \times 3$
$12 = 2 \times 2 \times 3$
$50 = 2 \times 5 \times 5$
$23 = 23$

Indices can be used to help write the factorisation of 12 and 50.

$12 = 2^2 \times 3$
$50 = 2 \times 5^2$

1 Write down each of the numbers between 20 and 30 as the product of prime factors.

 When you know the **prime factors** of a number you can work out all its **factors**.

For example, $12 = 2 \times 2 \times 3$

So the factors of 12 are these

1
2
3
$2 \times 2 = 4$
$2 \times 3 = 6$
$2 \times 2 \times 3 = 12$

2 Write down the factors of each of the numbers between 20 and 30.

3 (*a*) Write down the factors of 50.

   (*b*) What can you say about the factors of 50 and the factors of 12?

   (*c*) Find another number which has the same number of factors as 50.

4 (*a*) Write 54 as the product of prime factors.

   (*b*) How many factors does 54 have?

   (*c*) Find another number with the same number of factors as 54.

B5
page
46

5 Make up some more questions like these.

29

CLASSIFYING CUBOIDS

I Here is a collection of cuboids

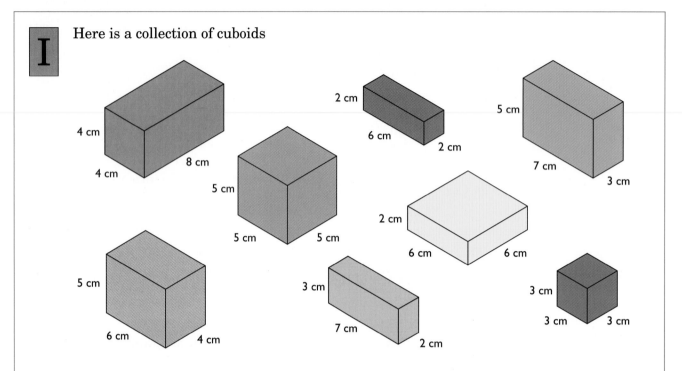

Somebody thinks of a question:

Which cuboids have a volume of more than 100 cm³?

This question divides the cuboids into two sets.

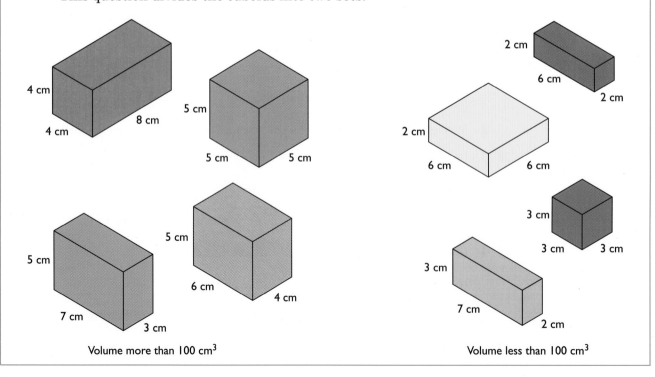

Volume more than 100 cm³   Volume less than 100 cm³

1 Here is another way of dividing the collection of cuboids into two sets.

What question might have been asked this time?

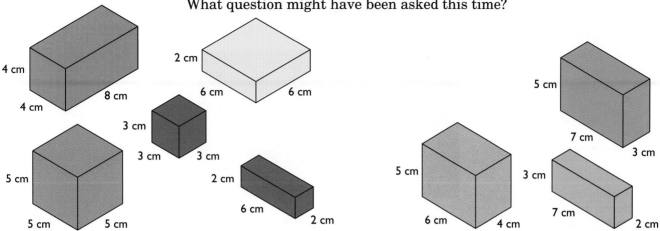

2 Think of your own question for dividing the collection of cuboids into two sets.

Show your two sets to other people. See if they can guess your question.

You could do this with several different questions.

3 Think of a question for dividing the collection of cuboids into three sets.

I Someone chooses one of the cuboids from the collection. Here are some questions which can be used to discover which cuboid was chosen.

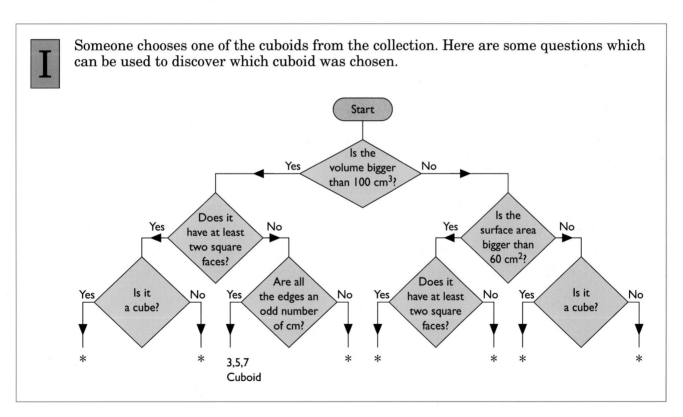

4 Copy the flowchart and complete it to show a cuboid at each of the places marked with a *.

E18
page
111

5 Make up a *different* flowchart which can be used to decide which cuboid from the collection has been chosen.

BOXES

If you cannot collect boxes you could use the resource sheet 'Boxes' for this activity.

You could use *Spread* or a spreadsheet for this activity.

Set it up in the same way as for '*Building cuboids*'.

1 litre = 1000 cm³

1 Collect some objects which are cuboids.

What are most of these objects made of? Why do you think this is?

2 Measure each object and calculate its volume.

3 Find the surface area of each of your boxes.

4 (*a*) Arrange your boxes in order of volume.

(*b*) Arrange your boxes in order of surface area.

5 Which three of your boxes have volumes which are closest to half a litre?

6 Work out the measurements for several different boxes which have a volume of half a litre.

7 Work out the measurements of some boxes which have a volume of half a litre and which are the same shape (as close as possible) as some of the boxes you have collected.

8 Someone measures the sides of a box to the nearest centimetre. She finds that the lengths of the sides are 13 cm, 18 cm and 8 cm.

(*a*) Find the volume of the box, assuming that these measurements are exact.

> I Because the lengths are measured to the nearest centimetre, the length of 13 cm could be anything between 12.5 cm and 13.5 cm.

(*b*) What is the largest volume the box could have?

(*c*) What is the smallest volume the box could have?

9 Look again at the objects you measured (or the objects on the resource sheet '*Boxes*').

(*a*) How accurately are the boxes measured?

(*b*) What is the largest volume each box could have?

(*c*) What is the smallest volume each box could have?

B6 page 46

C9 page 66

C10 page 67

CUBOIDS OF THE SAME SHAPE

I Two cuboids are the same shape if one is just a bigger version of the other.

Here are two cuboids which are the same shape. These are called **similar**.

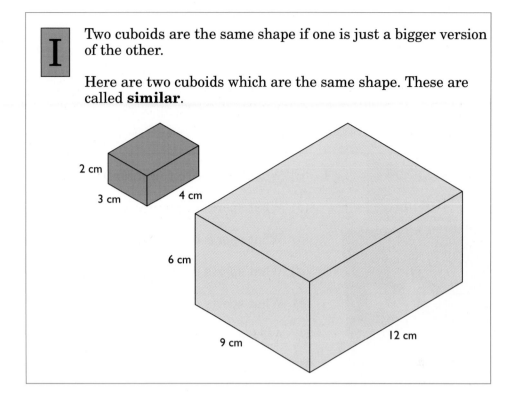

■ **1** Find another cuboid which is similar to the two cuboids in the box above.

■ **2** Find a cuboid which is similar to this cuboid.

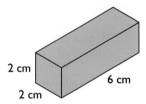

■ **3** Two cuboids are similar. Which of the following statements *must* be true?

A The two cuboids have the same surface area.

B The two cuboids have the same volume.

C The two cuboids have the same number of square faces.

■ **4** Collect different cuboid containers for the same product. (e.g. several cornflakes packets, several washing powder boxes, several stock-cube boxes).

● Are the packets for a particular product always the same shape?

● For which product are the packets closest to being the same shape?

● For which product are the shapes of the packets most different?

F22
page
133

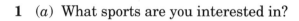

5 IT'S A RECORD!

This task is about sport. In many sports, records are important. These sports include athletics, swimming, cycling, skating and weightlifting.

WHAT SPORT DO YOU DO?

1 (*a*) What sports are you interested in?

(*b*) What sports do you take part in?

(*c*) What sports do you believe are the most popular in you class?

(*d*) What sports do you believe are the most popular in your school?

(*e*) What sports do you think people spend most time doing?

(*f*) Are boys interested in different sports from girls?

2 Which of your answers to question 1 do you *know* are correct?

I To find out if your other answers are correct you could carry out a survey.

You could start by designing a questionnaire. This is not as easy as it might sound. If you want the questionnaire to provide you with answers, you need to think carefully about what you want to find out.

The questions in the questionnaire need to be worded carefully, so that it is clear what the answers mean.

Here is an example where it would not be clear.

Do you play your favourite sport a lot?

Here are two alternative ways of asking this question so that it is clear what the answers mean.

Do you play your favourite sport at least once a week?

or

How often do you play your favourite sport:

    (a)   more than twice a week?
    (b)   more than once a week?
    (c)   more than once a month?
    (d)   less than once a month?

I The questions need to allow people to make up their own minds.

Here is an example where you try to make people's minds up for them.

Do you dislike hockey like most people?

Here are alternative ways of asking what people like, so that they can decide for themselves.

Which sports do you like:

    football

    tennis

    athletics

    hockey

    badminton

    other (please specify)?

or

    Write a list of the sports you like.

Make sure you design the questionnaire so that you get *all* the information you need.

You might want to use a database, such as *Pinpoint*, to help you.

Which sports do you like?

☐ football   ☐ hockey

☐ tennis   ☐ badminton

☐ athletics   ☐ squash

☐ other(please specify) _____

How often do you play your favourite sport?

☐ more than twice a week

☐ more than once a week

☐ more than once a month

☐ less than once a month

3 Design a questionnaire about the sporting interests of people in your class.

Give out your questionnaire for people to answer.

4 Analyse your results. You can draw graphs to display some of your findings.

You could use pictograms, bar charts, line graphs and pie charts.

C11
page
67

5 Write about the conclusions you have come to about favourite sports in your class.

ATHLETICS

Here are the World and United Kingdom records for men's track events. The records were correct in December 1991.

Men's Track Events

Event	World	United Kingdom
100 metres	9.86 s	9.97 s
200 metres	19.72 s	20.09 s
400 metres	43.29 s	44.50 s
800 metres	1 min 41.73 s	1 min 41.73 s
1000 metres	2 min 12.18 s	2 min 12.18 s
1500 metres	3 min 29.46 s	3 min 29.67 s
1 mile	3 min 46.32 s	3 min 46.32 s
2 kilometres	4 min 50.81 s	4 min 51.39 s
3 kilometres	7 min 29.45 s	7 min 32.79 s
2 miles	8 min 13.45 s	8 min 13.51 s
5 kilometres	12 min 58.39 s	13 min 0.41 s
10 kilometres	27 min 8.23 s	27 min 23.06 s
Marathon	2 hrs 6 min 50 s	2 hrs 7 min 13 s

Note: 1 mile = 1.6093 km
The marathon is run over 26 miles 385 yards.

1 In which events was the United Kingdom record the same as the World record?

Why do you think the records are the same?

2 In which events is the World record more than a quarter of an hour?

3 In which events is the difference between the World record and the United Kingdom record less than a second?

Except for the marathon, all the times in the table of men's track events are given correct to two decimal places of a second.

It might be more sensible to give the times for the longer distances correct to one decimal place. For example, for the 800 metres' World record (instead of 1 min 41.73 s) the time could be given as 1 min 41.7 s.

4 (a) Give all the men's record track times for events longer than 400 m correct to one decimal place of a second.

(b) Why might it be a more sensible degree of accuracy to give these times correct to one decimal place only?

 To find the average speed at which a race is run you divide the distance by the time.

For the 400 metres the United Kingdom record is 44.50 seconds. So the average speed is 400 ÷ 44.50 = 8.988 764 m s⁻¹. It might be sensible to give the answer correct to 3 significant figures. In this case it will be given as 8.99 m s⁻¹.

To help you answer question 5 you might want to put the results into a spreadsheet.

For question 5 you need to change times to seconds.

 There are 1760 yards in a mile.

5 (a) Find the average speed in metres per second for both the World record and the United Kingdom record for each distance. Give each of your answers correct to 3 significant figures.

(b) What happens to the average speed as the distance increases? Why do you think this is?

(c) If the 400 metres could be run at the same average speed as the 100 metres, what would the World record for the 400 metres be?

(d) If the Mile could be run at the same average speed as the 100 metres, what would the World record for the Mile be?

6 Find out your school records for track events..

Calculate the average speed for each event run by the school record holder.

B6 page 46   B7 page 47

ARE MEN BETTER AT SPORT THAN WOMEN?

I Here are the World records for men's and women's track events. The records were correct in December 1991.

World Record for Track Events

Event	Men	Women
100 metres	9.86 s	10.49 s
200 metres	19.72 s	21.34 s
400 metres	43.29 s	47.60 s
800 metres	1 min 41.73 s	1 min 53.28 s
1500 metres	3 min 29.46 s	3 min 52.47 s
1 mile	3 min 46.32 s	4 min 15.61 s
3 kilometres	7 min 29.45 s	8 min 22.62 s
5 kilometres	12 min 58.39 s	14 min 37.33 s
10 kilometres	27 min 8.23 s	30 min 13.74 s
Marathon	2 hrs 6 min 50 s	2 hrs 21 min 6 s

Note: 1 mile = 1.6093 km

The marathon is run over 26 miles 385 yards.

The fastest man is faster at all distances than the fastest woman. But how much faster? One way to measure this is to find the **ratio** of the time for a woman to the time for a man.

For example, for the 400 metres, the performance ratio is $47.60 \div 43.29 = 1.0995611$. Correct to 3 significant figures this is 1.10.

For these questions you need to convert time to seconds.

1 Find the performance ratio for each of the distances. Give each of your answers correct to 3 significant figures.

2 In the past women were not allowed to compete at long distances. People believed it would harm them, because women are not built to run long distances.

Compare the performance ratios (question 1) for short and long distances. Is there any evidence that women are not built for long distances?

3 Look at your school records. Find the performance ratio of girls to boys for each of the distances. How do these performance ratios compare with the World record performance ratios?

■ **4**   Look at this graph.

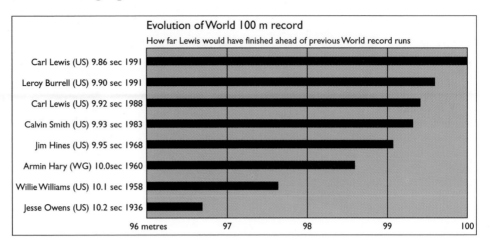

Evolution of World 100 m record

How far Lewis would have finished ahead of previous World record runs

Carl Lewis (US) 9.86 sec 1991
Leroy Burrell (US) 9.90 sec 1991
Carl Lewis (US) 9.92 sec 1988
Calvin Smith (US) 9.93 sec 1983
Jim Hines (US) 9.95 sec 1968
Armin Hary (WG) 10.0 sec 1960
Willie Williams (US) 10.1 sec 1958
Jesse Owens (US) 10.2 sec 1936

96 metres   97   98   99   100

Draw a graph like this, but put on it:

Carl Lewis's 1991 World record run.
The United Kingdom men's record holder in 1992 (Linford Christie).
The women's World record holder in 1992 (Florence Griffith-Joiner).
The holder of your school's boys' 100 metres record.
The holder of your school's girls' 100 metres record.

■ **5**   This table shows the British men who have held the World Mile record.

Year	Name of record holder	Record time
1884	George	4 min 12.75 sec
1937	Wooderson	4 min 6.4 sec
1954	Bannister	3 min 59.4 sec
1957	Ibbotson	3 min 57.2 sec
1981	Ovett	3 min 48.40 sec
1981	Coe	3 min 47.43 sec
1985	Cram	3 min 46.32 sec

There are 1760 yards in a mile.

Steve Cram's 1985 time was the current World Mile record in 1992.

Draw a graph, like that in question 4, to show the evolution of the mile record.

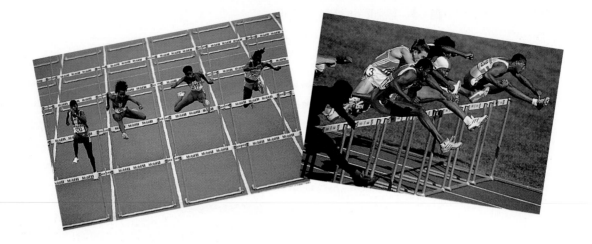

 Here are the World hurdles records for men and women.

	Men			Women	
	110 metres	12.98 s		100 metres	12.38 s
	400 metres	47.19 s		400 metres	53.17 s

6 Find the performance ratio for hurdles over the shorter and longer distances.

7 (a) Are women *without* hurdles at 100 metres quicker or slower than men *with* hurdles at 110 metres?

(b) Are women *without* hurdles at 400 metres quicker or slower than men *with* hurdles at 400 metres?

(c) Explain your answers to (a) and (b).

 Here are the men's and women's World records for some field events.

Event	Men	Women
High Jump	2.44 metres	2.09 metres
Long Jump	8.90 metres	7.52 metres
Shot-putt	23.12 metres	22.63 metres
Discus-throw	74.08 metres	76.80 metres
Javelin-throw	90.98 metres	80.00 metres

8 (a) Find the performance ratio for each of the field events.

(b) How do these performance ratios compare with those of the track events?

9 One performance ratio might surprise you. What might explain it?

G26
page
155

WHAT IS THE FASTEST WAY TO TRAVEL?

 Here are some World records from different sports

Cycling

Men's unpaced flying start 1 kilometre: 58.26 s.

Ice skating

Men's 1000 metres: 1 min 12.58 s.

Swimming

Men's 800 metres freestyle: 7 mins 50.64 s.

■ 1 Ice skating, cycling, running and swimming are four ways in which human beings can travel. List them in order of speed.

■ 2 In towns, car travel is sometimes a lot slower than cycling. Why is this?

■ 3 Find out how fast you travel in different ways. For example:

- you can time a car journey and use the trip mileage to find the distance
- you can time yourself running a certain distance
- you can time yourself cycling to school
- you can find the average speed on a aeroplane journey you have taken.

41

6 NUMBER GAMES

 You can play the game of guess my rule in several different ways.

Here is one way.
Someone goes out of the room. Everyone else decides on a rule about how to change numbers.
For example, they might decide to add 3.

The person who went out now returns to the room and says a number to anyone else in the room. This person has to use the rule and say what number it gives.

If Ann is the person guessing, the conversation might go like this for the 'Add 3' rule:

Ann '1'
Sharon '4'
Ann '8'
Tracy '11'
Ann '10'
Kirsty '13'
Ann '97'
David '100'

The person who went out (or Ann in the example) has to guess the rule.

The rules could be harder than this, as long as everyone can get the answers right.
    For example, you could have this rule:

if a girl is asked she adds 2,
if a boy is asked he doubles the number.

If Ann is the person guessing it might go like this:

Ann '5'   David '6'
Sharon '7'   Ann 'Are you sure?'
Ann '8'   David 'Yes.'
Tracy '10'   Ann '10'
Ann '13'   Sue '12'
Kirsty '15'   Ann '11'
Ann 'I've guessed it.' John '22'
Ann '3'

Play the game with other people in your class.

GUESS THE RULES

1 For each of the games below say what the rule is.

(a)
Ann '4'
Sharon '14'
Ann '2'
Tracy '12'
Ann '10'
Kirsty '20'
Ann '16'
David '26'
Ann '18'
Sue '28'
Ann '99'
John '109'

(b)
Ann '3'
Sharon '6'
Ann '8'
Tracy '16'
Ann '2'
Kirsty '4'
Ann '1'
David '2'
Ann '20'
Sue '40'
Ann '99'
John '198'

(c)
Ann '2'
Sharon '7'
Ann '10'
Tracy '23'
Ann '1'
Kirsty '5'
Ann '6'
David '15'
Ann '50'
Sue '103'
Ann '99'
John '201'

(d)
Ann '3'
Sharon '30'
Ann '5'
Tracy '50'
Ann '1'
Kirsty '10'
Ann '20'
David '200'
Ann '50'
Sue '500'
Ann '99'
John '990'

(e)
Ann '3'
Sharon '6'
Ann '9'
Tracy '12'
Ann '1'
Kirsty '4'
Ann '5'
David '12'
Ann '11'
Sue '14'
Ann '99'
John '106'

(f)
Ann '3'
Sharon '6'
Ann '8'
Tracy '11'
Ann '15'
Kirsty '30'
Ann '12'
David '15'
Ann '30'
Sue '33'
Ann '99'
John '198'

(g)
Ann '5'
Sharon '2'
Ann '8'
Tracy '4'
Ann '20'
Kirsty '10'
Ann '1'
David '0'
Ann '15'
Sue '7'
Ann '99'
John '49'

(h)
Ann '3'
Sharon '3'
Ann '6'
Tracy '6'
Ann '15'
Kirsty '51'
Ann '23'
David '32'
Ann '10'
Sue '1'
Ann '99'
John '99'

(i)
Ann '3'
Sharon '97'
Ann '6'
Tracy '94'
Ann '20'
Kirsty '80'
Ann '15'
David '85'
Ann '37'
Sue '63'
Ann '99'
John '1'

(j)
Ann '6'
Sharon '6'
Ann '8'
Tracy '2'
Ann '20'
Kirsty '12'
Ann '1'
David '19'
Ann '36'
Sue '35'
Ann '99'
John '63'

2 Write your own stories and give them to someone else to guess.

> **I** Suppose the rule is 'Add 4'.
>
> If you start with 3 you get 7
> If you start with 15 you get 19
> If you start with N you get $N + 4$.
>
> So you can write the rule like this:
>
> $N \rightarrow N + 4$

B8
page
47

This is hard for parts (g), (h) and (j).

3 Say that happens to N with each of the rules used in question 2.

YOU COULD USE:

You could use *Spread*.

Set up *Spread* with one row and two columns.

Enter a formula into column **B**. The formula you enter gives the rule for changing the numbers.

You could use your answers to question 3, in the last activity, as the formulas in column **B**.

SCORE THE FACTORS

 Here is a game for two teams: team A and team B.

You need to write out the numbers from 1 to 50 on a chart. Each team needs to see the chart clearly.

1	2	3	4	5	6	7	8	9	10
11	12	13	14	15	16	17	18	19	20
21	22	23	24	25	26	27	28	29	30
31	32	33	34	35	36	37	38	39	40
41	42	43	44	45	46	47	48	49	50

Team A chooses a number on the chart.
Suppose they choose 9.
Team B has to find the factors of 9. They score a point for each factor they can think of.
The factors of 9 are 1, 3 and 9.

So with 9 they could score 3 points.

Now cross out 9 on the chart.

1	2	3	4	5	6	7	8	✕	10
11	12	13	14	15	16	17	18	19	20
21	22	23	24	25	26	27	28	29	30
31	32	33	34	35	36	37	38	39	40
41	42	43	44	45	46	47	48	49	50

Team B now chooses a number and team A has to think of the factors. They cannot choose a number which is crossed out. Now team A chooses a number, and so on.

1 Play the game. Try to choose numbers carefully so that the other team cannot score too many points.

 Here is a second version of the game. In this version each team chooses the number for themselves instead of for the other team.

If the team chooses the number 20 they could score 6 points. This is because the factors of 20 are 1, 2, 4, 5, 10 and 20.

2 Play this version of the game.

B5
page
46

3 When you have played different versions of the game, write about which numbers are good to choose.

AND THE ANSWER IS ...

 Here is a game to play with your class. You need two or three teams of eight people. Other people can act as judges. Each team member has a sheet of paper with a label on it. Here are the labels each team needs

Here is how the game might start. Somebody says 'Make 50'.

Here is what the teams might do.

In this case two teams have hit the target of 50.

If more than one team hit the target exactly, the first team to finish wins a point.

If no team is exact, the team closest to the target wins a point.

1 Play the game.

2 What would you do for these targets?

   (*a*) Make 29.

   (*b*) Make 79.

   (*c*) Make 55.

   (*d*) Make 701.

   (*e*) Make 40.

   (*f*) Make 100.

   (*g*) Make the largest possible number.

   (*h*) Make the largest possible odd number.

   (*i*) Make a multiple of 9.

   (*j*) Make the largest possible multiple of 7.

   (*k*) Make 500.

   (*l*) Make 1000.

3 Make up your own targets and give them to someone else to solve.

If you want, you can change the labels the teams are to use.

REVIEW EXERCISES B

EXERCISE 5 Multiples and Factors

> Try to answer as many of these questions as possible without a calculator.

1 Which of these numbers are multiples of 9?

(a) 18   (b) 54   (c) 70   (d) 81

(e) 100   (f) 180   (g) 234   (h) 729

2 Which of these numbers are multiples of 20?

(a) 70   (b) 100   (c) 140

(d) 195   (e) 228   (f) 520

3 Which of these numbers are prime?

(a) 5   (b) 15   (c) 25   (d) 35   (e) 11

(f) 21   (g) 31   (h) 41   (i) 51   (j) 61

4 Here is a list of the first few multiples of a number. Some of the multiples have been left out. Copy the list and fill in the gaps.

?, ?, 27, ?, 45, ?, ?, 72

5 Here is a list of the first few multiples of a different number. Copy the list and fill in the gaps.

?, ?, ?, ?, ?, ?, 105, 120, ?, 150, ?

6 This is how 24 can be written as the product of prime factors.

$24 = 2^3 \times 3$

(a) Write these numbers as the product of prime factors:

(i) 20   (ii) 21   (iii) 36

(b) List all the factors of 20, of 21 and of 36.

EXERCISE 6 Estimating and Approximating

1 Each of these distances was produced by calculation, but the distances are only accurate to the nearest mile. Correct each distance to the nearest mile.

(a) 6.3 miles   (b) 17.8 miles

(c) 22.09 miles   (d) 13.5106 miles

2 Each of these numbers is only reliable to two decimal places. Correct each number to two decimal places.

(a) 4.523   (b) 6.457   (c) 3.6666

(d) 13.4209   (e) 15.5991   (f) 6.0012

3 Each of these numbers is only reliable to three significant figures. Correct each number to three significant figures.

(a) 1.542   (b) 7.7777   (c) 3.0891

(d) 0.02345   (e) 4.994   (f) 6.996

(g) 9349   (h) 92 453   (i) 0.008023

4 John says he lives 200 m from school.

(a) Do you think this measurement is correct to

(i)   the nearest centimetre?
(ii) the nearest metre?
(iii) the nearest 10 metres?
(iv) the nearest 100 metres?

(b) Use your answer to part (a) to answer the following.

(i) What is the smallest distance John might live from the school?
(ii) What is the largest distance John might live from the school?

5

| ASHBY | 5 | | MORTON | $2\frac{1}{4}$ |
| GOADBY | $3\frac{1}{2}$ | | WETTON | $\frac{3}{4}$ |

(a) The distance to Ashby is given as 5 miles. Do you think this is correct to

(i)   the nearest yard?
(ii) the nearest quarter mile?
(iii) the nearest half mile?
(iv) the nearest mile?

(b) Use your answer to part (a) to answer the following.

(i) What is the smallest distance to Ashby?

(ii) What is the largest distance to Ashby?

EXERCISE 7 Speed

1 The distance from London to Leeds is 190 miles. An Intercity train takes about $3\frac{1}{4}$ hours to travel from Leeds to London.

What is the average speed of the train?

2 (a) Mary drives four miles to work in the rush hour. Her journey takes her about half an hour. What is her average speed in miles per hour?

(b) Her husband John has the same distance to cycle to work. He says that he can do the journey in 18 minutes. What is his average speed in miles per hour?

3 Jenny walks 400 m to school each morning. To see how fast she walked, she timed her journey with a stop watch. She found that she took 5 minutes 13.8 seconds.

(a) How fast does Jenny walk to school?

(b) How accurately do you think it is sensible to give your answer to part (a)?

(c) If you were asked how long Jenny takes to walk 400 m how accurately would you give the answer?

4 A World-class runner can run 100 metres in about 10 seconds. A bus takes half an hour to travel the six miles to town.

Which is faster, the runner or the bus?

(1 mile = 1.6 km)

EXERCISE 8 Function Machines

1

The drawing above shows a function machine. It also shows what happens if 3 is input in the blue box.

(a) What numbers appear in the pink box, if the following numbers are input into the blue box?

(i) 6   (ii) 10   (iii) 50

(b) What numbers are input into the blue box to produce the following numbers in the pink box?

(i) 8   (ii) 16   (iii) 30   (iv) 250   (v) 17

2

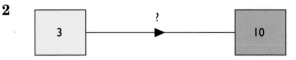

Here is a function machine. The diagram does not tell you what the machine does.

The table below shows what the machine does to numbers input into the yellow box:

Yellow box	Green box
3	10
5	16
10	31
30	91
100	301

(a) What does the machine do to numbers in the yellow box?

(b) If the following numbers are put into the yellow box, what numbers are produced in the green box?

(i) 1   (ii) 6   (iii) 20   (iv) 200   (v) 33

(c) What numbers in the yellow box produce the following numbers in the green box:

(i) 13   (ii) 19   (iii) 43

(iv) 40   (v) 400   (vi) 85   (vii) 1

(d) What number appears in the green box if the number *N* is put in the yellow box?

7 THE AREA OF A PIECE OF STRING

A METRE OF STRING

1 Make a loop of string one metre long.

You can use it to make different shapes.

> You need to cut more than one metre of string to tie it into a one metre loop.

> You might be able to answer some of these questions by thinking about the shapes made by your string instead of measuring them.

> You could lay your triangle onto a large sheet of centimetre- squared paper to find out.

---

2 Make a square with your metre of string.

How long, in centimetres, is one of the sides? What is the area of the square in square centimetres?

3 Make several rectangles with your string.

How long are the sides of each rectangle? What is the area of each rectangle?

4 Make an equilateral triangle with your string.

How long is each side? What is the area of the triangle?

5 Make some isosceles triangles with your string.

How long are the sides of each triangle? What is the area of each triangle?

6 Make some rhombuses with your string.

How long are the sides of each rhombus? What is the area of each rhombus?

7 Make a regular hexagon with your string.

How long are the sides of the hexagon? What is the area of the hexagon?

8 Make a circle with your string.

What is the diameter of your circle?
What is the radius of your circle?
What is the area of your circle?

9 Compare the areas of the shapes you have made. Which shape has the biggest area? Which has the smallest?

Which triangle has the biggest area? Which has the smallest?

Make other comparisons.

THE AREA OF A TRIANGLE

 Here are some triangles.

Here are the same triangles fitted into rectangles.

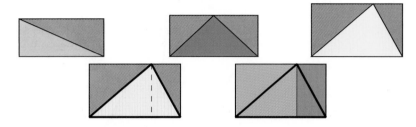

Each triangle is half the area of the rectangle it fits into.

This provides a method of finding the area of a triangle.
You need to know the lengths of the sides of the rectangle.
You can then find the area of the rectangle and halve it.

So the area of the triangle
is **base** × **height** ÷ **2.**

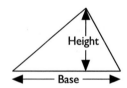

1 Copy each of these triangles onto centimetre-squared paper.

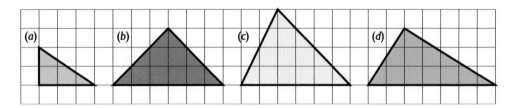

What is the height of each of your triangles?

Find the area of each of your triangles.

2 (a)

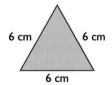

The equilateral triangle shown has a perimeter of 18 cm.
Draw it accurately. Measure its height and find its area.

(b) Draw several other triangles with a perimeter of 18 cm.

Draw and measure the height of each of your triangles.

Find the area of each of your triangles.

I This is a triangle with a perimeter of 18 cm. You might have drawn this triangle.

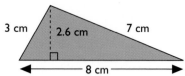

In this position the 'base' is 8 cm and the 'height' is about 2.6 cm.

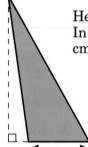

Here is the same triangle in two other positions. In these positions the 'base' is either 3 cm or 7 cm. The heights are outside the triangle.

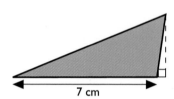

3 Draw accurately the triangle in the box above. Find the area of this triangle in three different ways, by using the three different 'bases' and 'heights'

4 Get the resource sheet *'Area of a triangle'*.

Draw the heights on each of the triangles on the resource sheet. Measure each triangle and find its area.

5 Use the formula for the area of a triangle to check some of your answers in *'A metre of string'*, on page 48.

THE AREA OF A CIRCLE

I Here is a way of thinking about the area of a circle.

Divide the circle up into lots of pieces.

If the pieces are small enough they are triangles (more or less).

The height of each triangle is the radius of the circle (more or less).

If you add together the bases of all the triangles you get the circumference of the circle.

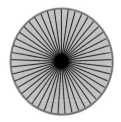

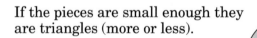

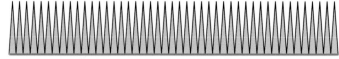

So the area of the circle is
circumference × radius ÷ 2.

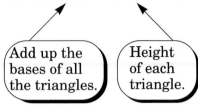

Add up the
bases of all
the triangles.

Height
of each
triangle.

The circumference of a circle (see *Task Maths* 1, page 142) is

π × diameter,
or π × 2 × radius.

So the area of a circle is

circumference × radius ÷ 2,

or π × 2 × radius × radius ÷ 2,

or π × radius × radius.

Remember:

Circumference of circle = π × diameter.
Area of circle = π × radius × radius.

1 Measure the radius of each of these circles.

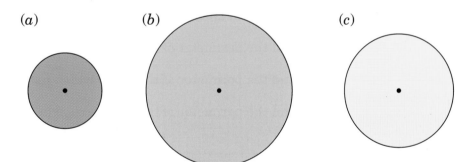

(a)   *(b)*   *(c)*

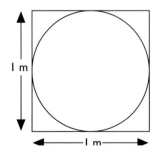

Use the formula in the Information box above to calculate the areas of
the circles.

2 Draw round some circular objects.

Calculate the circumferences and areas of the circles you have drawn.

3 Calculate the area of the biggest circle that fits into a metre square.

4 Calculate the area of the circle you can make with a metre of string.

Compare your answer with the answer you obtained before.

A SQUARE METRE

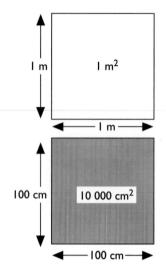

 The area of a metre square is 1 square metre, or 1 m².

1 Find the area of some things in the classroom. (Table top, blackboard, window, door, etc.)

Which of the things have an area which is more than 1 m²?

Which thing has an area closest to 1 m²?

2 Sketch and label some rectangles which have an area of 1 m².

Find the perimeter of each rectangle.

Which rectangle has the biggest perimeter?

Which rectangle has the smallest perimeter?

3 Sketch and label some other shapes which have an area of 1 m².

Find the perimeter of each shape.

4 Find the perimeter of the circle which has an area of 1 m².

5 Find the perimeter of the semicircle which has an area of 1 m².

A SQUARE METRE OF SURFACE

1 Find some solid objects.

Find the surface area of each of your objects.

Which objects have a surface area of more than a square metre?

2 Find an object which has a surface area as close to a square metre as possible.

3 Sketch and label some solids which have a surface area of 1 m².

A CUBIC METRE

 The volume of a metre cube is 1 cubic metre, or 1 m³.
This is quite a large volume.

1 Choose some large objects. Measure them and estimate their volumes.

2 Which objects have a volume bigger than 1 m³?

3 Which object has a volume closest to 1 m³?

C9
page
66

A LITRE

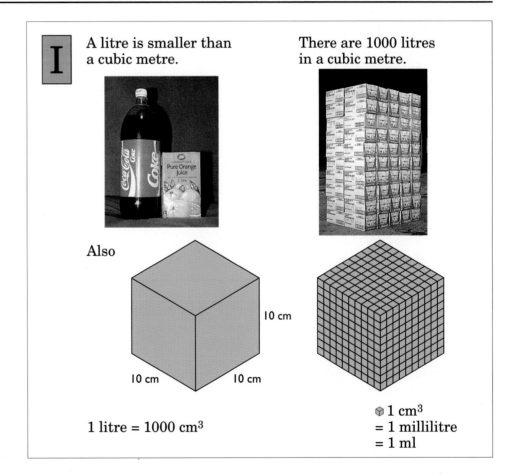

A litre is smaller than a cubic metre.

There are 1000 litres in a cubic metre.

Also

10 cm

10 cm   10 cm

1 litre = 1000 cm³

10 cm

1 cm³
= 1 millilitre
= 1 ml

1 Choose some containers (e.g. boxes, tins, bottles, etc.)

Measure each container and estimate its volume. Some containers have their volume printed on their labels.

2 Which containers have a volume bigger than 1 litre?

3 Which container has a volume closest to 1 litre?

8 WATCHING TELEVISION

HOW MUCH TV DO YOU WATCH?

It is suggested that you use minutes rather than hours, because this might make it easier to put the data into a database. You can use hours if you want. But remember that there are 60 minutes in an hour. So 3.5 hours means 3 hours 30 minutes.

1 How much TV do you watch in a week? Guess how many hours you watched TV last week.

Collect the results for the whole class.

Who thinks they watch most television? How many hours do they watch?

Who thinks they watch least television? How many hours do they watch?

2 To give a more accurate picture you can keep a record of your TV watching for a week. You will need to make decisions such as these:

Do you count watching videos as watching television?

Do you count having the TV on in the background while doing homework, etc?

To keep a record you could use a table like this one.

	Time watching TV (mins)	Time at home (mins)	Time asleep (mins)	Time at school (mins)
Monday Tuesday Wednesday				

TOP TEN

Instead of using the viewing figures provided, you could find your own more recent viewing figures and answer the questions using these.

	BBC1	Millions	BBC2	Millions	ITV	Millions	C4	Millions
1	EastEnders (Thu/Sun)	20.95	Top Gear (Thur/Fri)	6.52	Coronation St (Fri/Sun)	20.80	Cutting Edge	6.57
2	Neighbours (Mon)	18.82	Star Trek: the Next Generation	5.31	London's Burning	18.86	Brookside (Mon/Sat)	5.54
3	Casualty	16.06	Food and Drink (Tue/Thur)	5.27	The Ruth Rendell Mysteries	16.34	The Cosby Show	5.31
4	Jaws the Revenge	12.80	Clarissa	5.24	The Krypton Factor	14.83	Cheers	4.03
5	Noel's House Party	11.16	Thunderbirds	4.88	The Bill (Tue)	14.64	Fifteen-to-One (Mon)	3.78
6	The Generation Game	12.09	Murder Most Horrid	4.79	Blind Date	14.52	Clive Anderson Talks Back	3.63
7	Last of the Summer Wine	10.55	Attack on Fear	4.68	Home and Away (Tue)	14.28	The Golden Girls	3.35
8	Canned Carrott	10.39	Quantum Leap	4.21	Strike it Lucky	13.96	Drop the Dead Donkey	3.34
9	Nine O'Clock News	10.37	Cats	4.16	Beadle's About	13.24	Little House on the Prairie	3.28
10	A Question of Sport	9.83	Operation Petticoat	4.06	This is Your Life	13.22	Somebody Up There Likes Me	3.26

Source: **Broadcaster's Audience Research Board (BARB) for 25 Nov/1 Dec 1991**

	BBC1	Millions	BBC2	Millions	ITV	Millions	C4	Millions
1	EastEnders (Thu/Sun)	20.51	Top Gear (Thur/Fri)	7.06	Coronation St (Wed/Sun)	21.47	Brookside (Fri/Sat)	5.49
2	Neighbours (Mon)	18.17	Thunderbirds	5.57	You've Been Framed	17.28	The Cosby Show	5.30
3	Casualty	15.17	Go toward the Light	5.50	Big	16.46	Prime Suspect	5.08
4	Only Fools and Horses	13.27	Sure Thing	5.32	The Bill	15.16	The Golden Girls	4.41
5	Canned Carrott	12.48	Food and Drink (Tue/Thur)	5.16	Home and Away (Mon)	14.66	The Lord of the Rings	4.18
6	Crimewatch UK	11.36	Star Trek: the Next Generation	5.15	This is Your Life	14.50	Fifteen-to-One (Wed)	4.01
7	Bruce Forsyth's Generation Game	11.31	Clarissa	4.86	Blind Date	13.96	Cheers	3.89
8	Noel's House Party	11.11	Quantum Leap	4.30	Strike it Lucky	13.56	Voyage to the Bottom/Sea	3.67
9	Starman	11.04	Have I Got News for You? (Fri/Sat)	4.29	Wish You Were Here..?	13.54	Desmond's	3.60
10	News and Weather (Sun)	11.01	The Travel Show Guides	4.05	Bullseye	12.20	Clive Anderson Talks Back	3.50

Source: **Broadcaster's Audience Research Board (BARB) for 2-8 Dec 1991.**

1 Which was the most popular programme on

(a) BBC1 in the week 25 Nov. – 1 Dec. 1991?

(b) BBC2 in the week 2 – 8 Dec. 1991?

(c) C4 in the week 2 – 8 Dec. 1991?

2 Which was the most popular programme on *any* channel in the week 25 Nov. – 1 Dec. 1991?

3 Make a list of the top 10 programmes on *any* channel for the week 2 – 8 Dec 1991. Here is the start of this list.

Programme	Millions
Coronation Street	21.47
East Enders	20.51
Neighbours	18.17

4 Why can you not tell which programme was the *least* popular on television during the week 2 – 8 Dec. 1991?

For questions 5 to 7 consider the week 2 – 8 Dec. 1991, or use your own viewing figures.

5 Look at the top ten programmes on BBC1.

What was the mean number of people watching these programmes?

6 Answer question 4 for each of the other three channels.

7 (*a*) Which channel was the most popular in the week 2 – 8 Dec. 1991?

(*b*) Which channel was the least popular?

Give reasons for your answers.

8 Was more television watched during the week 25 Nov. – 1 Dec., or during the week 2 – 8 Dec.?

Explain how you decided on your answer.

How certain do you think your answer is?

I The population of the United Kingdom is about 57 million.

For questions 9 and 10 consider the week 2 – 8 Dec. 1991, or use your own viewing figures.

9 (*a*) What percentage of the population of the UK watched Coronation Street?

(*b*) What in the population of the town or village you live in?

(*c*) Estimate how many people in your town or village watched Coronation Street.

10 (*a*) What percentage of the population of the UK watched Brookside?

(*b*) Estimate how many people in your town or village watched Brookside.

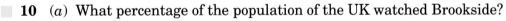

NOW AND THEN

Use some up-to-date television viewing figures. You might be able to find these in the Radio Times or the TV Times.

Write about some of the differences between television viewing in December 1991 and television viewing now.

You could, for example, consider

- which programmes from December 1991 are still being shown
- whether the number of people watching television has increased.

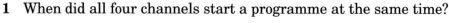

CHRISTMAS EVE TELEVISION

For this activity you need the resource sheet 'Christmas Eve television'.

A3 page 26

1 When did all four channels start a programme at the same time?

2 (a) Which was the shortest programme on Christmas Eve?

   (b) Which was the longest programme?

3 The following sports were featured on Christmas Eve: baseball, cricket and golf.

   Which of these sports had least time given to it? How much time was that?

4 Ann wanted to watch as many films as possible on Christmas Eve. But she would only watch a film if she could see all of it.

   How many films could she watch?

5 Which channel showed films for longest on Christmas Eve?

   How long were films shown for on this channel?

6 What was the longest programme shown on Christmas Eve?

7 Which channel has the longest programmes on average?

TV FACTS

I Here are the results of a National Survey about television viewing in 1988.

I prefer watching TV to reading.

	Boys	Girls
11-year-olds	47%	34%
15-year-olds	67%	50%

How much television do you watch?

11-year-olds (all)	3 hrs 24 mins per day
15-year-old boys	3 hrs 4 mins per day
15-year-old girls	2 hrs 47 mins per day

How much reading do you do?

| 11-year-olds (all) | 3.9 hours per week |

What do you watch?

	15-year-olds	
	Boys	Girls
Comedy	60%	60%
Soaps	30%	60%
Documentaries	13%	13%
News	7%	7%
Sport	35%	10%
Cartoons	50%	50%
Films	50%	50%

You might want to use statistics for your own class or your own school for this activity.

1 (a) What percentage of 11-year-old girls prefer watching TV to reading?

(b) What percentage of 15-year-old boys prefer reading to watching TV?

2 (a) Do 11-year-olds spend more time on reading than on watching TV?

(b) How long do 11-year-olds spend reading in a year?

(c) How long do 11-year-olds spend watching TV in a year?

3 Suppose a school has 600 students and about half of the students are girls.

Estimate how may students

(a) watch cartoons

(b) watch comedy

(c) watch soaps

(d) watch news

4 A city has 2000 11-year-olds living in it. Estimate how many of the 11-year-olds prefer reading to television.

5 (a) Between the ages of 11 and 15 both boys and girls get converted from reading to TV. Are more boys converted or more girls?

(b) Estimate the percentage of 13-year-old boys who prefer reading to TV.

(c) Estimate the percentage of 14-year-old girls who prefer reading to TV.

(d) Estimate the percentage of 20-year-olds who prefer reading to TV.

HOW MUCH TV DO YOU WATCH?

1 Record the results for your whole class in a database.

2 Which is the most popular day for watching TV in your class?

3 Produce a line graph showing the amount of TV you watch on different days of the week.

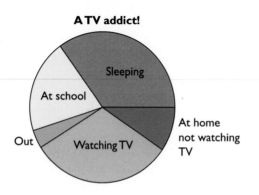

A TV addict!

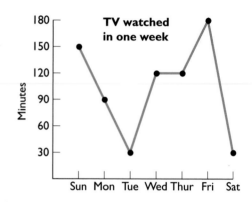

TV watched in one week

4 Produce a pie chart showing the percentage of time you watch TV, sleep, spend at home not watching TV, spend at school, and spend out.

This is how you can draw a barchart showing how long everyone in your class watched television on Saturday.

You first decide on a suitable time interval. This could be 20 minutes.

Now put everyone's TV viewing on a tally chart, like this:

Time watching TV (mins)	Tally	Frequency
0–19	II	2
20–39	IIII	4
40–59	HHT HHT I	11
60–79	HHT	5
80–99	I	1
100–119		0
120–139		0
140–159	III	3
160–179	I	1

You can then draw a barchart to show the results.

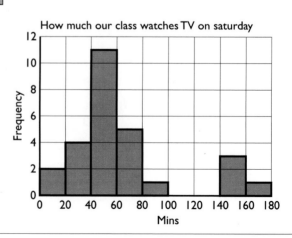

How much our class watches TV on saturday

5 Draw a barchart showing how long people in your class watched television on Saturday.

6 Draw barcharts or frequency polygons to compare Saturday viewing with Sunday viewing.

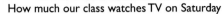

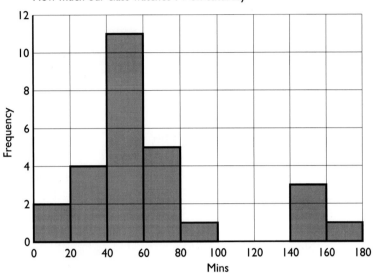

How much our class watches TV on Saturday

A database such as *Pinpoint* will produce such charts for you.

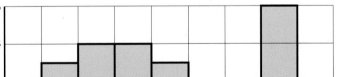

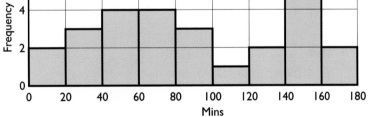

How much our class watches TV on Sunday

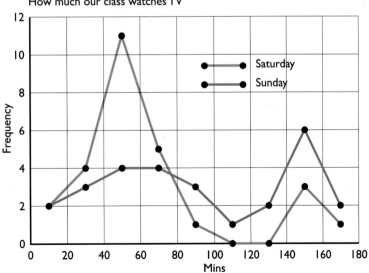

How much our class watches TV

Saturday
Sunday

C11
page
67

9 SURROUNDED!

SURROUNDING SHAPES

On a piece of squared paper colour some of the squares black.

You could choose this or this.

Now colour in red all the squares which touch one of the black squares.

Stage 1

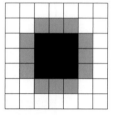
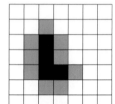

Now colour in blue all the squares which touch one of the red squares.

Stage 2

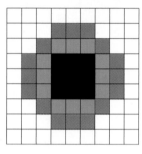
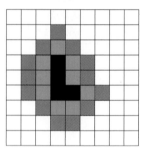

Repeat for a different colour.

Stage 3

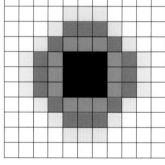
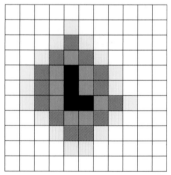

Keep repeating this as many times as you want.

Now look at the drawings you have produced.

- How many squares do you add at each stage?

- Is there a rule?

- Can you predict the number of squares you would add at the next stage.

- Can you predict the number of squares you would add at

    (i) stage 20?
    (ii) stage 100?
    (iii) stage *N*?

JUSTIFYING YOUR RESULTS

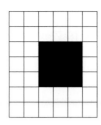

If you start with the square shape shown you add 12 red squares, then 16 blue squares, then 20 yellow squares.

You add 4 more squares at each stage. These pictures show why.

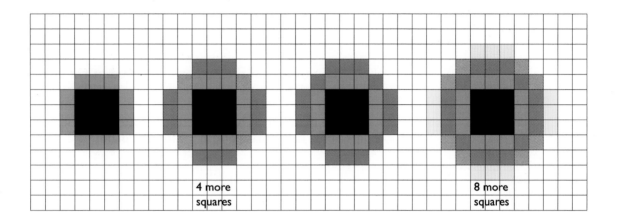

4 more squares

8 more squares

■ Draw your own pictures to show why your rule works for your pattern.

WHAT HAPPENS IF...?

Many starting shapes produce a very tidy rule for the number of squares coloured at each stage.

Some awkward shapes do not give such a tidy rule.

1 For each of these shapes find the number of squares coloured for the first few stages. What happens eventually? When does it start to happen?

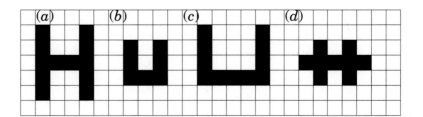

(a) (b) (c) (d)

2 Make up some awkward shapes of your own. For your shapes find the number of squares coloured for the first few stages. What happens eventually? When does it start to happen?

SURROUNDING SQUARE CLUSTERS

Suppose your starting pattern consists of 2 squares.

The squares can be joined together or they can be separate.

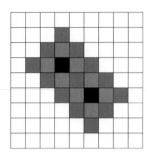

The number of red squares coloured at the first stage is 6 for one pattern and 8 for the other.

The number of blue squares coloured at the second stage is 10 for one pattern and 13 for the other.

1 Try different patterns of two squares.

(*a*) How many red squares does each pattern produce at the first stage?

(*b*) How many blue squares does each pattern produce at the second stage?

(*c*) Continue each pattern until you can see what happens eventually. When does it happen?

(*d*) Draw a diagram to show how many squares are added at each stage for different patterns. Here is one way you could do this.

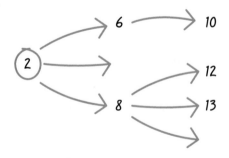

Your diagram can show more than the first two stages.

2 Answer question 1 but start with different patterns of three squares.

SURROUNDING WITH TRIANGLES

 You can surround shapes with triangles instead of squares.

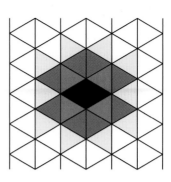

1 (*a*) Surround each of the following shapes with triangles.

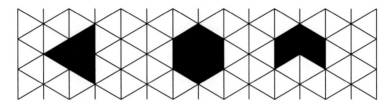

For this activity you will need some isometric line paper.

(*b*) For each shape, say how many triangles are coloured at the first stage, second stage and third stage.

(*c*) For each shape, find a rule for the number of triangles coloured at different stages.

(*d*) The rules for each shape are different. For each shape, how many squares are added at

    (i)   the 20th stage?
    (ii) the 21st stage?
■   (iii) the *N*th stage?

2 Make up some starting shapes of your own and surround them with triangles.

What is the rule for each of your shapes?

■ **3** Can you predict what the rule will be for a new shape?

G27
page
155

SURROUNDING WITH OTHER SHAPES

1 Start with a hexagon. Surround it with hexagons.

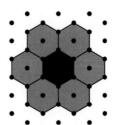

You could use ATM MATs for this activity or the computer program 'Tiling'. For question 1 you might want to use isometric paper instead.

Surround with hexagons again. And again.
How many hexagons do you need at each stage?
What is the rule?

2 Start with a pentagon. Surround it with pentagons.

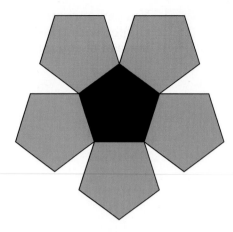

Surround with pentagons again. What happens with pentagons?

3 Look at this picture of octagons and squares.

For question 3 you need the resource sheet '*Octagons and squares*'.

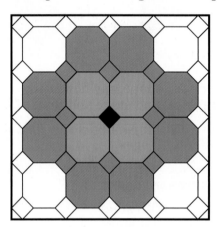

(*a*) Explain how the picture has been coloured.

(*b*) What is the rule for this picture?

(*c*) Make a picture starting with an octagon instead of a square. What is the rule this time?

4 For each of these tessellations make pictures like those in question 3.

For question 4 you need the resource sheets '*Hexagons and triangles*', '*Hexagons, squares and triangles*' and '*Squares and triangles*'.

You can make more than one picture for each tessellation, depending on which shape you start with.

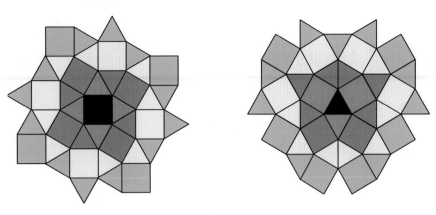

Find rules for some of your pictures.

SURROUND-ING WITH CUBES

For this activity you need some interlocking cubes.

■ **1** Start with one cube. Surround it by putting a cube on each of its faces.

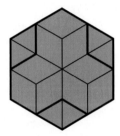

Count the number of cubes you have added.

Now surround your model again by putting a cube on each of its faces.

One way of picturing the result after this second stage is as follows.

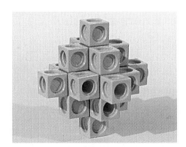

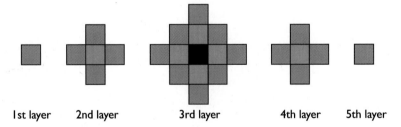

1st layer　　2nd layer　　　3rd layer　　　4th layer　　5th layer

How many cubes are added at this second stage?

How many cubes are added at the third stage? You might find it helpful to draw some pictures of the layers of the model.

How many cubes are added at the next two stages?

Can you find a rule for this process?

■ **2** Start with two or three cubes joined together.

Surround the model as in question 1.

How many cubes are added at each stage?

Can you find a rule?

REVIEW EXERCISES C

EXERCISE 9 Area and Volume

1 Find the areas of these triangles.

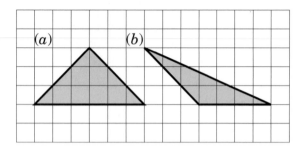

2 Find the areas of these triangles.

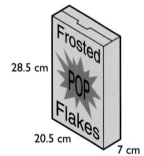

(a) 5 cm, 6 cm

(b) 7 cm, 9 cm

3 Find the volume and surface area of this cereal packet.

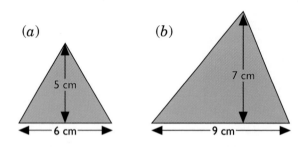

28.5 cm
20.5 cm
7 cm

Frosted POP Flakes

4 Find the volume of this chest of drawers.

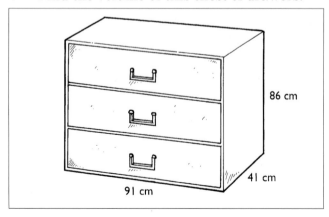

86 cm
41 cm
91 cm

5 Find the circumference and area of each of the following.

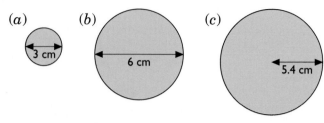

(a) 3 cm

(b) 6 cm

(c) 5.4 cm

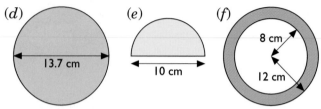

(d) 13.7 cm

(e) 10 cm

(f) 8 cm, 12 cm

6 The circumference of a bicycle wheel is 200 cm. Find the radius of the wheel.

7 The circumference of a circular garden pond is 15 metres. Find the area of the pond.

EXERCISE 10 Units and Conversions

1 1 litre = 1000 cm^3

Change the following to cm^3.

(a) 2 litres of coke.

(b) $\frac{1}{2}$ litre of cooking oil.

(c) 0.7 litre of wine (a normal bottle).

(d) 5 litres of car oil.

2 1 tonne = 1000 kg
A tin of baked beans weighs 400 g. When the tins are sent to shops they are packed in boxes each containing 60 tins.

A warehouse is storing 7000 boxes of beans. Find, in tonnes, the approximate weight of beans in the warehouse.

3 This chart converts gas regulo marks for a gas oven to centigrade temperatures for an electric oven.

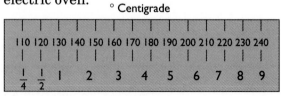

° Centigrade

110 120 130 140 150 160 170 180 190 200 210 220 230 240

$\frac{1}{4}$ $\frac{1}{2}$ 1 2 3 4 5 6 7 8 9

Gas regulo

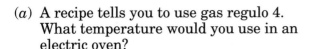

(a) A recipe tells you to use gas regulo 4. What temperature would you use in an electric oven?

(b) A casserole is to be cooked at 200°C. What regulo would you use in a gas oven.

4 1 oz is about 28 grams

(a) Draw a conversion graph to convert from ounces to grams.

Use 1 cm to represent 1 ounce on the horizontal axis and 1 cm to represent 20 g on the vertical axis.

(b) Use your graph to construct a chart for converting ounces to grams, like the chart in question 3.

(c) How many grams is 5 ounces?

(d) How many ounces is 100 grams?

EXERCISE 11 Presenting Data

1 The table below shows how long you can run various electrical appliances on one unit of electricity.

2 kw convector heater	$\frac{1}{2}$ hour
1 kw infra-red heater	1 hour
Iron	2 hours
3 kw radiant heater	20 minutes
Tumble drier	$\frac{1}{2}$ hour
Vacuum cleaner	3 hours

Draw a pictogram to display this information. Each picture should represent $\frac{1}{2}$ hour of time.

Give the pictogram a clear title and a clear key.

2 Different countries have different amounts of health care. This table shows how many people there are for each doctor.

USA	650
Sweden	850
UK	860
Japan	910
Brazil	2090
India	4830
Nigeria	30000
Kenya	50000
Ethiopia	65400

(a) Draw a bar graph to display this information. Use one square to represent 2500 people. Label your bar graph, so that it clearly communicates the information.

(b) Calculate how many doctors there are for every 100 000 people in each country. (For example, there are 100 000 ÷ 650 = 154 doctors for every 100 000 people in USA.)

(c) Draw a bar graph to show how many doctors there are for each 100 000 people in different countries.

(d) The population of Birmingham in the UK is about 2 million. How many doctors look after the people of Birmingham?

(e) The population of Delhi in India is about 6 million. How many doctors look after the people of Delhi?

3 300 school leavers were asked how they spent their weekly wage. These are typical results.

Paying for keep	£11.20
Going out	£11.80
Clothes, make-up	£. 9.50
Records, tapes, CDs	£ 2.10
Travel	£ 6.50
Savings	£10.10
Other	£ 2.20

(a) What was the total amount spent each week?

(b) What percentage of the total amount was spent on each of the items in the list?

(c) Use the resource sheet *'Percentage pie charts'* to draw a pie chart to display the information given in the table. Label the pie chart clearly.

10 WHEN ARE THINGS THE SAME?

SAME AREA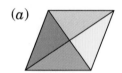

1 Which of these shapes have the same area?

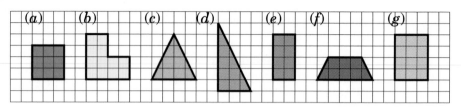

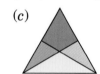

I Look at this drawing. The *red* and *blue* pieces have the same area. The *green* and *yellow* pieces have the same area.

2 In each drawing say which pieces have the same area.

(a) (b) (c) (d)  (e)

I This picture shows two rectangles which have the same area.

This picture shows a triangle and a rectangle which have the same area.

3 Draw a rectangle and a square which have the same area.

4 Draw a square and a triangle which have the same area.

5 Draw a rhombus and a square which have the same area.

6 Draw an equilateral triangle and a regular hexagon which have the same area.

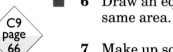

C9 page 66

7 Make up some more problems like this and give them to someone else to solve.

SAME SHAPE AND SIZE

 Two shapes which are the same shape and size are called **congruent**.

The blue triangles are congruent and the red rectangles are congruent. The yellow squares and the green triangles are not congruent.

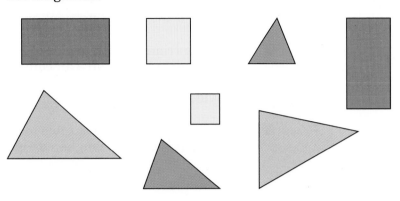

 This pictures show a rectangle and its diagonals.

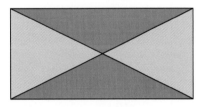

There are four pieces. The pieces are two different shapes. The two *red* pieces are congruent. The two *blue* pieces are congruent.

1 Draw a square and its diagonals.

There are four pieces. Colour the pieces to show which ones are congruent.

2 Draw a parallelogram and its diagonals.

There are four pieces. Colour the pieces to show which ones are congruent.

The resource sheet 'Shapes' might be useful for question 3.

3 How many different shapes are the pieces in the following drawings?

(*a*) A kite and its diagonals.

(*b*) A rhombus and its diagonals.

(*c*) An isosceles trapezium and its diagonals.

(*d*) A right-angled trapezium and its diagonals.

(*e*) A regular pentagon and its diagonals.

(*f*) A regular hexagon and its diagonals.

4 Draw an isosceles triangle. Divide it into two congruent pieces.

5 Draw an equilateral triangle.

   (a) Divide it into three congruent pieces.

   (b) Divide it into six congruent pieces.

6 Draw a scalene triangle.

   Divide it into four congruent pieces.

7 Draw a triangle with angles of 30°, 60° and 90°. (This is the triangle you get when you halve an equilateral triangle.)

   Divide it into three congruent pieces.

8 Copy and complete this table to show how many congruent pieces different types of triangles can be divided into.

F22
page
133

Number of congruent pieces	Isosceles	Equilateral	Scalene
2	Yes		No
3		Yes	
4			Yes
5			
6		Yes	
7			
8			
9			
10			

THE SAME AMOUNT

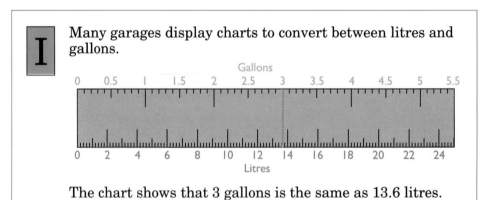

I Many garages display charts to convert between litres and gallons.

The chart shows that 3 gallons is the same as 13.6 litres.

1 Use the chart in the box above.

   (a) How many litres is 5 gallons?

   (b) How many gallons is 20 litres?

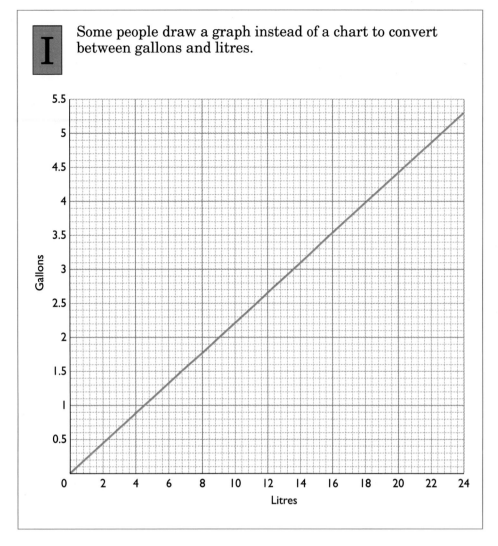

I   Some people draw a graph instead of a chart to convert between gallons and litres.

2   Use the graph in the box above.

(*a*) How many gallons is 18 litres?

(*b*) How many litres is 1 gallon?

3   If you go to Germany you need Deutschmarks (DM). In 1990 £1 was worth 3 DM.

Draw both a graph and a chart to convert between £ and DM.

> You could find out the current value of £1 in DM and use this for your graph and chart.

4   Sometimes it is useful to convert temperatures between Farenheit and Celsius.

Here is the connection:

32°F is the same as 0°C,
212°F is the same as 100°C.

Draw both a graph and a chart to convert between °C and °F.

C10
page
67

5   (*a*) Which do you find easier to read, a chart or a graph?

(*b*) Which do you find easier to draw, a chart or a graph?

THE SAME NUMBER

Do not use a calculator for the questions on this page until you have to.

1 Calculate these:

(a) 3×5 (b) 5×3

(c) 7×11 (d) 11×7

(e) 13×19 (f) 19×13

2 (a) What do you notice about the answers to question 1?

(b) Write down some more pairs like these which give the same answer.

3 Calculate these:

(a) $4 + 8$ (b) $8 + 4$

(c) $113 + 135$ (d) $135 + 113$

(e) $237 + 763$ (f) $763 + 237$

4 (a) What do you notice about the answers to question 3?

(b) Write down some more pairs like these which give the same answer.

5 Calculate these:

(a) $8 - 3$ (b) $3 - 8$

(c) $22 - 5$ (d) $5 - 22$

(e) $37 - 100$ (f) $100 - 37$

6 What do you notice about the answers to question 5?

7 Calculate these:

(a) $8 \div 2$ (b) $2 \div 8$

(c) $25 \div 5$ (d) $5 \div 25$

(e) $10 \div 4$ (f) $4 \div 10$

8 What do you notice about the answers to question 7?

9 Calculate these:

(a) $13 + 5 - 7$ (b) $13 - 5 + 7$ (c) $13 - 7 + 5$

(d) $5 + 13 - 7$ (e) $7 - 5 + 13$ (f) $5 - 7 + 13$

10 (a) Look at the answers to question 9. When do you get the same answer?

(b) Make up some calculations like these using different numbers instead of 5, 7 and 13.

11 (a) Which of these are the same?

(i) 3^2 (ii) 3×2 (iii) 2^3 (iv) 2×3

(b) Use different numbers instead of 2 and 3. Find out when the answers are the same.

Brackets tell you to do the calculation inside the brackets first.

For example $13 - (7 - 5)$ means 11 and not 1.

12 Calculate the following:

(*a*) $5 + (4 + 3)$

(*b*) $(4 + 3) - 5$

(*c*) $5 \times (4 + 3)$

(*d*) $5 - (4 - 3)$

(*e*) $5 - (4 + 3)$

(*f*) $5 \times (3 + 2) - 3 \times (4 - 1)$

13 (*a*) Which of these are the same?

(i) $3 \times (4 + 5)$

(ii) $3 \times 4 + 3 \times 5$

(iii) 3×9

(*b*) Now make up your own examples like these, using different numbers instead of 3, 4, 5 and 9.

 For questions 14 and 16 you might need to use the $\boxed{+/-}$ button on your calculator to get negative numbers.

14 Calculate these, using your calculator:

(*a*) $3 - 5$

(*b*) $4 - (-5)$

(*c*) $6 + (-4)$

(*d*) $8 - (-2)$

(*e*) $2 + (-7)$

(*f*) $(-4) + (-6)$

15 Now try to calculate these without using your calculator:

(*a*) $5 - 9$

(*b*) $8 + (-7)$

(*c*) $3 - (-8)$

(*d*) $4 + (-9)$

(*e*) $7 - (-5)$

(*f*) $(-8) + (-7)$

16 Calculate these, using your calculator:

(*a*) $3 \times (-5)$

(*b*) $(-4) \times 5$

(*c*) $6 \times (-4)$

(*d*) $(-8) \times (-2)$

(*e*) $(-2) \times (-7)$

(*f*) $(-5) \times 6$

17 Now try to calculate these without using your calculator:

(*a*) $3 \times (-2)$

(*b*) $(-5) \times 5$

(*c*) $(-3) \times (-4)$

(*d*) $(-6) \times 8$

(*e*) $7 \times (-5)$

(*f*) $(-8) \times (-7)$

D12
page
90

EQUATIONS

Look at this pair of numbers

8 and 3 + 5.

The two numbers are the same.

Now look at this pair of numbers

4 + ☐ and 11.

There is a number missing. There is a ☐ instead. To make this pair of numbers the same you need to put 7 in place of the ☐, like this

4 + 7 and 11.

1 Put numbers in the boxes to make each pair of numbers the same.

(a) 6 + ☐ and 11   (d) 20 and ☐ × 4

(b) 15 and 5 + ☐   (e) 18 − ☐ and 9

(c) 3 × ☐ and 12   (f) 8 and ☐ − 6

A letter is often used instead of a box. To show that a pair of numbers are the same the equals sign, =, is often used. So instead of

4 + ☐ and 11   you can write   4 + n = 11.

This is called an **equation**. In this equation, putting 7 instead of n makes the equation true. So the solution of the equation is n = 7.

2 Find the solution of these equations.

(a) n + 7 = 12   (c) 24 + n = 24

(b) a − 3 = 20   (d) 100 − x = 37

3 Find the solution of these equations. Some of the solutions are negative numbers.

(a) 6 − x = 2   (c) 2 − x = 6

(b) 30 + a = 20   (d) x + 100 = 31

When a letter is used for a number the multiplication sign, ×, is often left out.

2p means the same as 2 × p.

4 Solve these equations. Some of the solutions are not whole numbers.

(a) 3p = 12   (c) 4a = 12

(b) 2n = 7   (d) 12a = 4

5 Solve these equations. They are a bit more complicated.

    (*a*) $2m + 5 = 11$ (*c*) $2x + 5 = 12$

    (*b*) $20 - 4x = 14$ (*d*) $5x - 3 = 47$

 Sometimes the equations are more complicated still. The letter is in more than one place.

One way of solving these equations is to try different numbers instead of the letter until you find the one that works.

6 Solve these equations:

    (*a*) $2n + 5 = n + 8$ (*c*) $x + 11 = 5x - 1$

    (*b*) $3x - 4 = 2x + 3$ (*d*) $4x + 5 = 2x + 1$

Equations are harder to solve if the answer is not a whole number. In this case a calculator might help.

This is how you could solve the equation

$3m + 14 = 8m + 5$.

If you guess $m = 1$ you get $17 = 13$, and the number on the right is too small.

If you guess $m = 2$ you get $20 = 21$, and the number on the right is only slightly too big.

So you know the solution is between 1 and 2 and is nearer to 2. So you could try numbers like 1.7, 1.8 and 1.9.

If you try $m = 1.8$ you get $19.4 = 19.4$ and so 1.8 is the solution.

You could also use *Spread*. Use eleven rows and three columns.

To solve the equation

$3m + 14 = 8m + 5$

enter these formulae

B = 3 * A + 14
C = 8 * A + 5

Now block enter some numbers in A and press U. Keep doing this until you get the same number in columns B and C. The solution is then in column A.

7 Solve these equations:

    (*a*) $6x + 5 = x + 16$ (*d*) $x + 25 = 5x + 6$

    (*b*) $5x - 7 = x + 12$ (*e*) $4x + 7 = 7x - 9$

    (*c*) $6x + 13 = 37 - 4x$ (*f*) $7x + 8 = 2x + 2$

E19
page
111

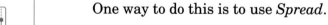

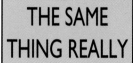

THE SAME THING REALLY

■ 1 Look at this rectangle.

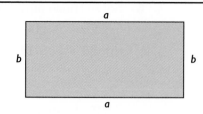

You find its perimeter by adding together the lengths of its sides.

Here are some answers for the perimeter.

$a + b + a + b$ $2a + 2b$ $2ab$

$4ab$ $2(a + b)$ $2(a + 2b)$

Some of these answers are correct and some are wrong. Which answers are correct?

I One way of checking whether two formulae mean the same thing is to substitute numbers in. Here is an example.

Are these two formulae the same thing?

$2a + 2b$ $4ab$

Check by substituting $a = 5$ and $b = 2$.

$2a + 2b = 2 \times 5 + 2 \times 2 = 10 + 4 = 14$
$4ab = 4 \times 5 \times 2 = 40$

These answers are *not* the same. So the formulae do *not* mean the same thing.

Only one substitution that gives *different* answers is needed to check that formulae are *different*. But you might want to use several substitutions to check that formulae are the *same*.

One way to do this is to use *Spread*.

This is how you could check that $2a + 2b$ *does* mean the same thing as $2(a + b)$.

Set up *Spread* with 4 columns and several (say 10) rows.
Enter the formula 2A+2B in column C.
Enter the formula 2∗(A+B) in column D.
Block enter some numbers in column A and some different numbers in column B.
Press U to update the table.

If columns C and D have *exactly* the same numbers then the formulae probably do mean the same thing.

■ 2

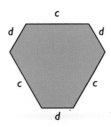

Write down the perimeter of this shape in several different correct ways.

■ 3

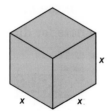

Write down the total length of the lines in this diagram in several different correct ways.

■ 4 (a) Do both these formulae correctly give the volume of the cube?

x^3 $3x$

(b) Write down the surface area of the cube in several different correct ways.

■ 5 Some of these formulae mean the same thing as each other. Rewrite the formulae, grouping together those that mean the same thing.

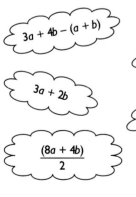
$3a + 4b - (a + b)$

$3(a + b)$

$2(2a + b)$

$2a + 3b$

$3a + 2b$

$6ab$

$5a + b$

$a + a + 2a + 3b$

$\dfrac{(8a + 4b)}{2}$

$a + 2b + 2a + b$

$4a + 2b$

$6a - (a - b)$

$2a + b + 2a + b$

$6a + 2b - (a + b)$

$5a + 3b - a - b$

■ 6 Question 5 was about a collection of formulae. Make up your own collection of formulae, some of which mean the same thing.

When you have made your collection give it to somebody else to sort out.

D13
page
90

FAIR DICE

NORMAL DICE

1 Describe a normal dice.

- What does it look like?
- What is it used for?
- What makes it a fair dice?

2 Look at a dice. Which number is opposite the 6? What other numbers are opposite each other?

3 These are the nets of some dice.

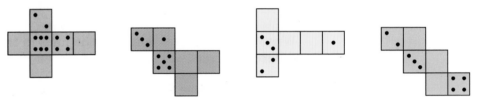

You could make dice from the nets on the resource sheet 'Dice' to help you answer question 3.

(*a*) Copy the nets and put in the missing spots.

(*b*) These are some more nets for dice.

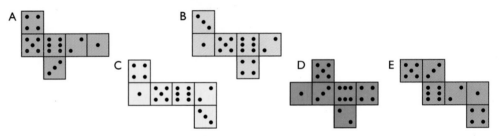

'I'll win if the number the dice shows is even.'

'I'll win if the number the dice shows is odd'.

If you made the dice from these nets, which dice would look *exactly* the same?

4 Ann and Dave play a dice game. They keep throwing the dice.

(i) What is the probability that Ann wins?

(ii) What is the probability that Dave wins?

(iii) Is the game fair?

5 Answer question 4 for each of these new rules.

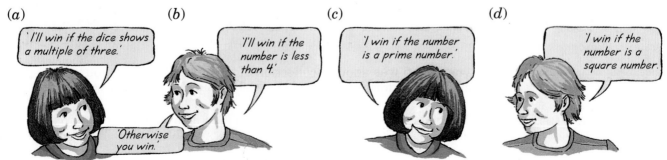

(*a*)

'I'll win if the dice shows a multiple of three.'

'Otherwise you win.'

(*b*)

'I'll win if the number is less than 4.'

(*c*)

'I win if the number is a prime number.'

(*d*)

'I win if the number is a square number.'

REARRANGING THE SPOTS

1 How many spots are there on a normal dice?

 Here are the nets of two unusual dice. They have the same number of spots as a normal dice, but the spots are arranged differently.

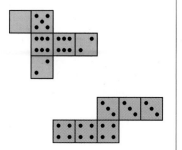

2 Make up your own unusual dice. Each dice should have the same number of spots as a normal dice.

 Here is a game for two players.

Each player has a dice.
Each player throws the dice once.
The winner is the person who throws the higher number.

3 Ann and Dave play this game with a normal dice. They play it 100 times.

(a) Which person would you expect to win most often? Explain your answer.

(b) Would you expect Ann to win   more than 50 times,
or exactly 50 times,
or less than 50 times?

Explain your answer.

 A table of outcomes

A table could be used to show when Ann wins and when Dave wins.

		Dave					
		1	2	3	4	5	6
	1	D	L	L	L	L	L
	2	W	D	L	L		
A	3	W	W				
n	4						
n	5						
	6						

To help with part (c) you might want to copy and complete the table of outcomes in the

(c) What is the probability that Ann wins when they play the game once?

You could use tables of outcomes for question 4.

4 Ann and Dave agree to play the game again. Dave says he will use a normal dice. Ann says she will use an unusual dice, but it must have the same number of spots as the normal dice.

How should Ann arrange the spots so she can expect to win most often? You will need to try out several possibilities.

Find the probability of Ann winning if she uses the best possible dice.

D14
page
91

CUBOID DICE

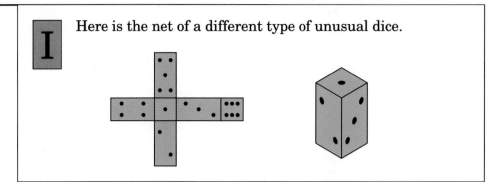

I Here is the net of a different type of unusual dice.

You might want to make a dice like this and try it out.

1 What is unusual about this dice?

2 Do you think that this dice is fair? Explain your answer.

3 If you used this dice, which numbers would you expect to get most often?

4 Sketch the net of a dice which you would expect to give the numbers 1, 2, 5 and 6 most often.

For questions 4 and 5 you could draw sketches instead of accurate drawings.

5 Sketch the net of a dice which you would expect to give the numbers 1 and 6 most often.

6 (*a*) Get the resource sheet '*Cuboid dice*'.

Cut out the nets and make the dice.

The resource sheet contains dice for several different values of *x*.

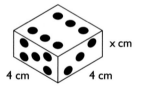

You can cut down the amount of work for this question by sharing your results with other people.

(*b*) Throw each of your dice 100 times. Record how often you get a 6.

(*c*) Draw a graph showing the number of times you get a 6 with each dice.

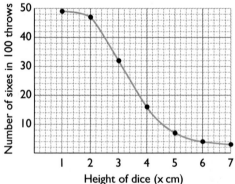

(*d*) Estimate the probability of getting a 6 with each of your different dice.

(*e*) Choose values of *x* which nobody in the class used to make their dice. Use your graph to estimate the probability of getting a 6 with these values of *x*.

FAIR DICE

1 With a normal dice, why do you have an equal chance of getting any of the six numbers?

2 Which of these solid shapes would make a fair dice?

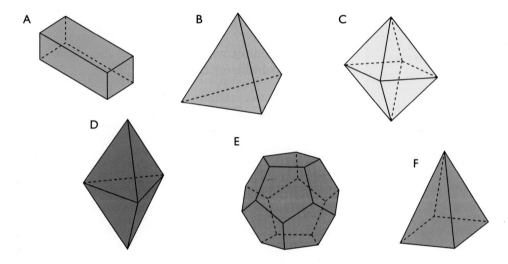

3 (a) Here is the net of a regular tetrahedron.

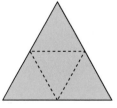

Is a regular tetrahedron a fair dice?

(b) You can make an irregular tetrahedron by using a triangle of a different shape.

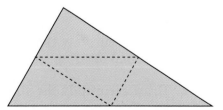

Make an irregular tetrahedron of this type.

Is your tetrahedron a fair dice?

81

PRISMS AND OTHER DICE

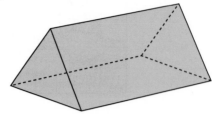

I Suppose you want a dice with five sides. You could use a triangular prism.

To make the prism fair you have to get the length right.

You could use ATM MATs for this activity. You could start with four squares and two equilateral triangles. You could also try four rectangles and two equilateral triangles. You could then try cutting the rectangles to get a fairer dice.

1 Experiment with triangular prisms of different lengths. Try to find a triangular prism which is fair.

2 Experiment with making fair dice from other shapes such as cylinders or pyramids or cones.

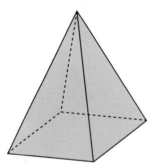

SPINNERS

I A spinner is a type of dice in a way. The spinner shown has 5 numbers.
The shape for this spinner is a regular pentagon.

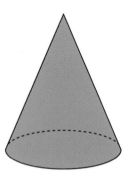

To do this, first draw a circle. Then use a protractor.

1 Draw accurately the shape for a spinner which could be used instead of a normal dice.

2 Draw accurately the shape for a spinner with 3 numbers.

3 Draw accurately the shape for a spinner with 4 numbers.

4 Draw accurately the shape for a spinner with 5 numbers.

A2 page 25

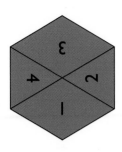

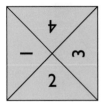

5 This spinner could have six numbers but it only has four numbers.

(*a*) What is the probability of getting a 1?

(*b*) What is the probability of getting a 2?

■ **6** Here is a spinner with 4 sides, numbered 1, 2, 3 and 4. What is the probability of getting a prime number from one spin?

What is the probability of getting a prime number from a spinner with 5 sides, numbered 1, 2, 3, 4 and 5?

What about 6 sides? 7 sides? ...

Draw a graph, showing the probability of getting a prime number using spinners with different numbers of sides.

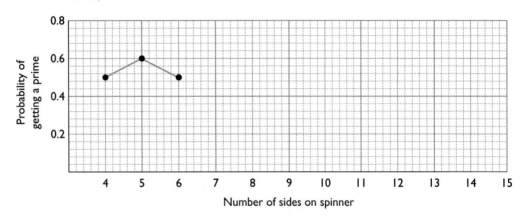

7 Make up some spinner problems of your own.

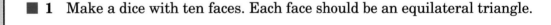

■ **1** Make a dice with ten faces. Each face should be an equilateral triangle.

> **I** If you place the dice on a table there are two top faces.
>
> You could decide that to get the score for the dice you *add* the numbers on the two top faces. In this picture the score is 8.
>
>

■ **2** Number the faces of your dice so that the ten scores you can get are 1, 2, 3, 4, 5, 6, 7, 8, 9 and 10. (You cannot do this by using whole numbers.)

■ **3** Investigate dice like this make from different numbers of triangular faces.

PAINTING BY NUMBERS

MODULO ARITHMETIC

Pictures like this can be made using modulo arithmetic.

I Addition modulo 4 means that after three you go back to 0 again.

 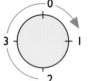 $2 + 3 = 1$

Here is the addition table for modulo 4.

+	0	1	2	3
0	0	1	2	3
1	1	2	3	0
2	2	3	0	1
3	3	0	1	2

1 (a) Write out the addition tables for modulo 3, modulo 5 and modulo 6.

(b) Describe the patterns you can see in these tables.

Here is how modulo arithmetic tables can be used to colour pictures.

Start with a modulo arithmetic table.

	0	1	2
0	0	1	2
1	1	2	0
2	2	0	1

Colour each square according to its number.

     0 = red, 1 = yellow, 2 = blue

A bigger picture can be made by translating this square to the right

and then translating down.

A different picture can be made by reflecting the square

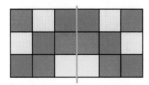

and then reflecting again.

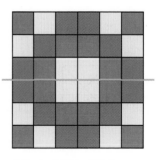

2   (*a*) Make your own pictures by using a modulo addition table. Different people in the class can use different tables.

    (*b*) Collect together all the different pictures made by your class. What similarities and differences are there in the pictures?

Here is the table for multiplication modulo 4.

×	1	2	3
1	1	2	3
2	2	0	2
3	3	2	1

3 (*a*) Write out multiplication tables for modulos 3, 5, 6, 7, 8 and 9.

(*b*) Describe the patterns you see in your tables.

4 (*a*) Which multiplication tables have a zero in them?

(*b*) Does the table for multiplication modulo 15 have any zeros in it? If so, where do they occur?

(*c*) How many zeros are there in the table for multiplication modulo 12?

(*d*) How many zeros are there in the table for multiplication modulo 16?

(*e*) Predict how many zeros any modulo multiplication table will have.

5 (*a*) Make a picture using a modulo multiplication table. Use the translating and reflecting ideas described in the box before question 2. Different people in the class can use different tables.

A1 page 25

B5 page 46

(*b*) Collect together all the different pictures made by your class. What similarities and differences are there in the pictures?

 The picture at the beginning of this task was produced using an addition modulo 8 table reflected twice. It uses these designs to represent numbers.

| 0 | 1 | 2 | 3 | 4 | 5 | 6 | 7 |

6 Design your own picture.

You could use different symbols as well as different colours

You could use modulo addition tables or modulo multiplication tables.

You could use 'partial' multiplication tables like this one.

D15 page 91

×	1	3	5	7
1	1	3	5	7
3	3	1	7	5
5	5	7	1	3
7	7	5	3	1

PASCAL'S TRIANGLE OF NUMBERS

You will find the resource sheet *'Hexagons'* useful for this activity.

 Here is the beginning of Pascal's triangle of numbers.

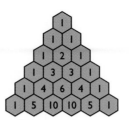

1 Extend Pascal's triangle until you reach the row starting 1, 10, ...

2 (*a*) Colour in the sequence of numbers 1, 2, 3, 4, 5, 6 . . . . in your Pascal's triangle.

(*b*) Pick out other sequences from your Pascal's triangle. How would they continue if you extended your triangle?

 This Pascal's triangle is formed using arithmetic modulo 3.

+	0	1	2
0	0	1	2
1	1	2	0
2	2	0	1

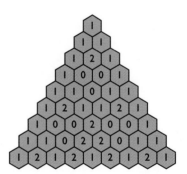

This picture is formed when the numbers are replaced by colours.

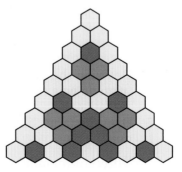

87

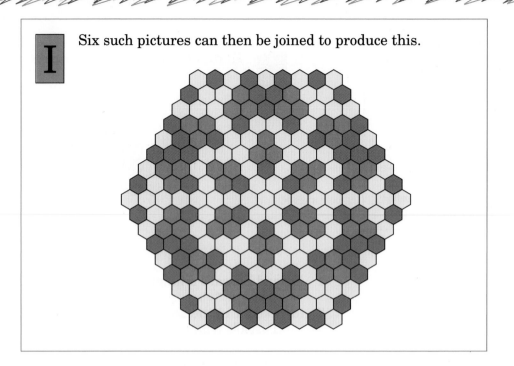

I Six such pictures can then be joined to produce this.

3 Make a picture from Pascal's triangle using arithmetic modulo 4 or 5 or 6 or . . . .

Write about patterns in your picture.

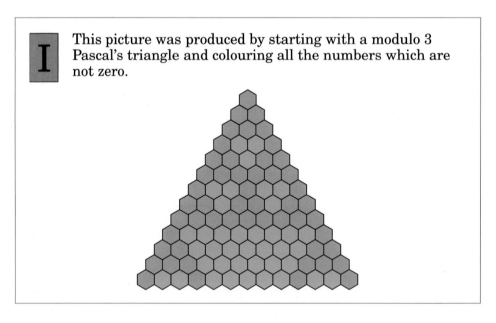

I This picture was produced by starting with a modulo 3 Pascal's triangle and colouring all the numbers which are not zero.

4 Describe the picture in the box above. How would it continue if Pascal's triangle was extended?

5 Draw pictures like this using Pascal's triangle with other modulo numbers.

Different members of the class can draw different pictures.

Collect all the pictures together. In what ways are they the same? In what ways are they different?

G27
page
155

UPSIDE-DOWN TRIANGLES

 Look at these triangles.

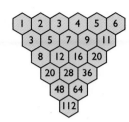

These triangles are like upside-down Pascal's triangles.

Here is a picture of one of the triangles, if the multiples of 3 are coloured red.

1 Make some upside-down triangle pictures.

2 Can you make an upside-down triangle with *no* multiples of 3?

3 Can you make an upside-down triangle which consists of *only* multiples of 3?

4 (*a*) Can you make an upside-down triangle with no multiples of 3, and with *all* the numbers in the triangle *different*?

   (*b*) Can you make an upside-down triangle which consists of *only* multiples of 3, and with *all* the numbers in the triangle *different*?

5 Suppose an upside-down triangle starts with a row of four numbers.

   What choices of four numbers produce a multiple of 3 at the bottom?

   Now try the same problem with a different number of starting numbers.

6 Can you have an upside-down triangle where no numbers are multiples of 4?

7 Investigate multiples of 5 in upside-down triangles.
   Multiples of 6. Of 7 . . .

REVIEW EXERCISES D

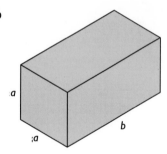

2

(a) What is the perimeter of this rectangle?

(b) What is the area of this rectangle?

EXERCISE 12 Operations and Negative Numbers

Try to answer the following questions without a calculator. You can then use a calculator to check your answers.

1 (a) $3 - 5$ (b) $7 - 13$

(c) $16 - 7 - 11$ (d) $(-5) + 8$

(e) $(-11) + 3$ (f) $(-4) + (-8)$

(g) $(-10) + (-12)$ (h) $(-5) - (-4)$

2 (a) $12 - (8 + 3)$ (b) $10 - (4 + 12)$

(c) $6 - (3 - 2)$ (d) $8 - (4 - 10)$

3 (a) $4 \times (-2)$ (b) $6 \times (-5)$

(c) $(-4) \times 7$ (d) $(-3) \times (-4)$

(e) $(-5) \times 8$ (f) $(-9) \times (-4)$

3 If $x = 3$, evaluate the following

(a) $3x$ (b) x^3

(c) $2x$ (d) x^2

(e) x^4 (f) $4x^2$

(g) $\dfrac{x + 2}{x}$ (h) $\dfrac{1 - x}{1 + x}$

4 Write the following without brackets:

(a) $2(p + q)$ (d) $6(r - 3s)$

(b) $3(2x + y)$ (e) $4(a + 2b) + 2(2a + b)$

(c) $4(u - v)$ (f) $5(3a + b) - 3(a + 5b)$

5 Which of the following are correct formulae for the surface area of this cuboid?

(a) $4a + 2b$

(b) $a^2 + a^2 + ab + ab$

(c) $a^4 + a^4b^4$

(d) $2a^2 + 4ab$

(e) $4(a^2 + ab)$

(f) $2(a^2 + 2ab)$

(g) $2a(a + 2b)$

EXERCISE 13 Using Symbols

The perimeter of this square is
$a + a + a + a = 4a$.

The area of this square is $a \times a = a^2$.

1

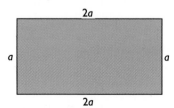

(a) What is the perimeter of this rectangle?

(b) What is the area of this rectangle?

EXERCISE 14 Probability

1 Three friends decide to play a game with a dice. When the dice is thrown, Lynne wins if the number is 1 or 2, and Diane wins if the number is 3 or 4. Otherwise, Karl wins.

Is the game fair? Explain your answer.

2

On end   On side

There are two ways a drawing pin can fall.

Someone threw a drawing pin 40 times. It landed on its side 24 times and on its end 16 times.

(a) Using these results:

    (i) work out an estimate for the probability of a drawing pin falling on its side.

    (ii) work out an estimate of the probability of a drawing pin falling on its end.

(b) The drawing pin is now thrown 100 times. Estimate the number of times it will fall on its side.

3 Two dice are thrown. The numbers obtained are added together to get the score. Copy and complete this table to show all the possibilities.

Second dice

	1	2	3	4	5	6
1	2	3	4	5	6	7
2	3	4	5	6		
3						
4						
5						
6						

First dice (labels to the left, rows 3 and 4)

(a) What is the probability that the score is 12?

(b) What is the probability that the score is 4?

(c) Which is the most likely score? What is the probability of getting this score?

4

Two four-sided spinners are thrown.

The numbers obtained are *multiplied* together to get the score.

You could draw a table similar to the table in question 6 to help answer the following.

(a) What is the probability that the score obtained is a multiple of 3?

(b) What is the probability that the score obtained is a multiple of 4?

EXERCISE 15 Transformations

1 Copy the blue line and the red shapes.

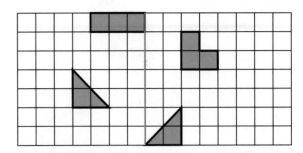

Draw the images you get when you reflect the red shapes in the blue line.

2 The quadrilateral Q has vertices at the points (2,1), (3,4), (6,3) and (7,1).

(a) Draw Q on squared paper.

(b) Draw the reflection of Q in the x-axis. Call this quadrilateral R. Write down the coordinates of the vertices of R.

(c) Draw the image of Q if it is translated one square to the right and four squares down. Call this quadrilateral S. Write down the coordinates of the vertices of S.

3 The triangle T has vertices at (2,2), (2,5) and (4,5).

(a) Draw T on squared paper.

(b) The triangle U is obtained by reflecting T in the y-axis. Draw U. Write down the coordinates of U.

(c) The triangle V is obtained by reflecting U in the x-axis. Draw V. Write down the coordinates of V.

(d) There is a transformation that takes triangle T directly to triangle V. Describe this transformation as precisely as you can.

(e) The triangle W is obtained by translating the triangle U ten squares to the right. Draw W. Write down the coordinates of W.

(f) There is a transformation that takes triangle T directly to triangle W. Describe this transformation as precisely as you can.

WHERE OUR SCHOOL IS

Where is your school? Which places are near your school? How far is your school from various other places? How do students in your class get to school? How long is the average journey to school for students in your class? Does your school have school buses?

These pages provide the answers to these questions for *Longslade School* in Birstall, Leicestershire. You could collect data, and answer similar questions for your school.

ROUTE TO SCHOOL

1 Jane lives in Birstall. She lives in Dalby Avenue. Her house is marked with a red cross, on the map on page 93. She walks to school.

Describe Jane's route to school.

2 Sue lives in Hazel Close. Her house is marked with a blue cross. She walks to school. There are two sensible routes she can take. Describe the two routes.

3 This is how Dave describes his route home from school.

> Turn right out of the school drive.
> Take the second turning on the right.
> When the road ends, turn left
> go along this road and then
> take the second turning on the left.
> Then take the first turning
> on the right.
> Our house is a little way along
> that road on the left.

(*a*) What road does Dave live in?

(*b*) Describe Dave's route *to* school.

4 Sidhartha lives in Tempest Road. His house is marked with a green cross. He cycles to school. Describe one route which he could take.

E18
page
111

I   1 metre = 1.09 yards
    1760 yards = 1 mile
    63360 inches = 1 mile

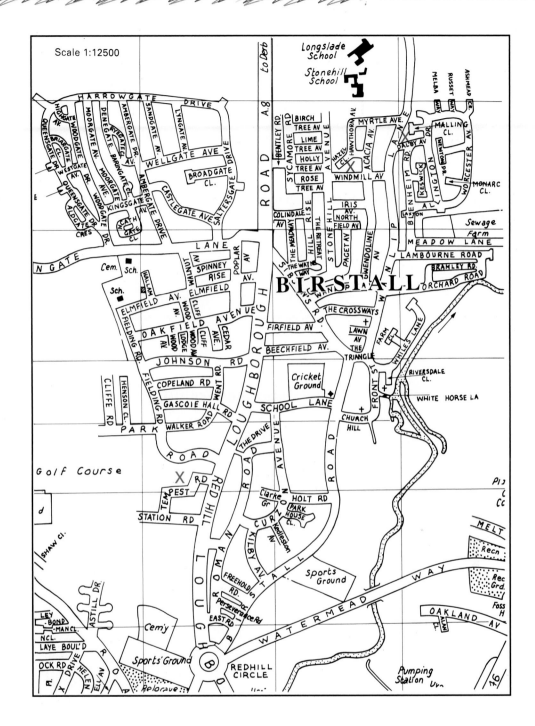

B7
page
47

C10
page
67

For questions 5 and 6 you will find the resource sheet 'Measuring in decimals of an inch' helpful.

5 (a) How far do Jane, Sue and Dave travel to school?

(b) Assuming that each of them walks to school at about 2 miles per hour, how long do they each take?

6 (a) How far does Sidhartha travel to school?

(b) Assuming that he cycles at about 10 miles per hour, how long does he take?

FROM THE SCHOOL'S POINT OF VIEW

Some people like looking at views from the tops of hills.

Often there is a **topograph**, which tells you which direction places are in, and how far away they are.

Here is a Leicestershire topograph for Longslade School. All the places shown on the chart are in Leicestershire.

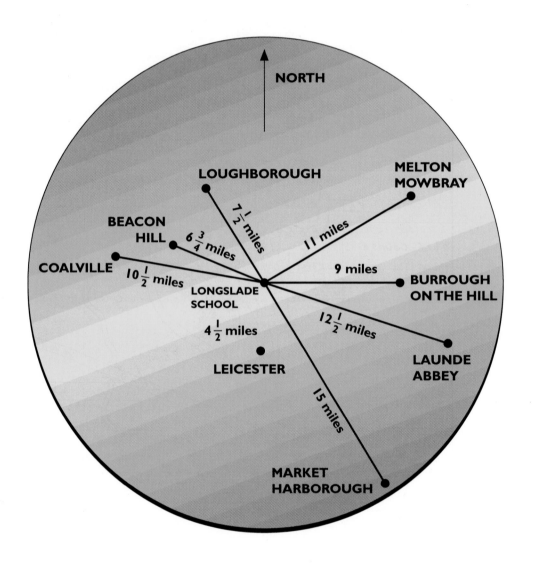

For this activity you will find the resource sheet 'Measuring in decimals of an inch' helpful.

1 The distances are all measured 'as the crow flies'. What does this mean?

2 Which of the places on the Leicestershire chart is furthest away?

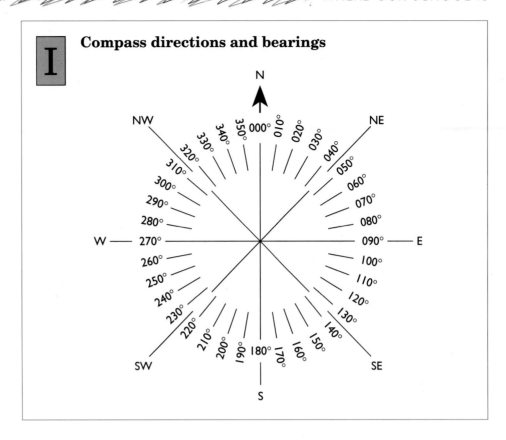

Compass directions and bearings

---

3 (a) Which place is due East of Longslade School?

(b) Which place is North East of Longslade School?

4 What is the bearing of each of the places from Longslade School?

5 What scale has been used for the Leicestershire topograph?

6 What is

(a) the distance as the crow flies

(b) the bearing

of each of these places from Longslade School?

Ipswich	Norwich
Manchester	Nottingham
Northampton	Oxford
	Skegness

7 The regional topograph for Longslade School shows London and Birmingham. What is the scale of the regional topograph?

8 Put the places listed in question 6 in their correct positions on the regional topograph.

> You could draw a county topograph for your school.

> For question 6 you need the resource sheet 'Map of the Midlands and East Anglia'.

> For questions 7 and 8 you need the resource sheet 'Regional topograph'.

> Your could draw a regional topograph for your school.

E16
page
110

WHERE WE LIVE

1 (*a*)   How many people from each group live in Birstall?

These lists show where students from two of the tutor groups in Longslade School live. It also shows the distances they live from Longslade School.

Tutor group 1	Miles	Tutor group 2	Miles
Allington Drive, Birstall	$\frac{1}{2}$	Gladstone Street, Anstey	5
Maplewell Road, Anstey	5	Station Road, Cropston	$4\frac{1}{2}$
Macauley Road, Rothley	$3\frac{1}{2}$	Leicester Road, Thurcaston	3
Knights Crescent, Rothley	$3\frac{1}{4}$	The Close. Anstey	$5\frac{1}{4}$
Braemar Close, Mountsorrel	$4\frac{1}{4}$	Latimar Road, Cropston	$4\frac{1}{2}$
Roman Road, Birstall	$1\frac{1}{2}$	Birkdale Road, Anstey	5
Ludgate Close, Birstall	$1\frac{1}{4}$	Birkdale Road, Anstey	$5\frac{1}{2}$
Worcester Avenue, Birstall	$\frac{3}{4}$	Tournament Road, Glenfield	6
Myrtle Avenue, Birstall	500 yards	Ballandine Road, Anstey	5
Gorse Hill, Anstey	$5\frac{3}{4}$	The Close, Anstey	$5\frac{1}{4}$
Green Gate Lane, Birstall	$\frac{3}{4}$	Lawn Avenue, Birstall	$\frac{1}{2}$
Highgate Avenue, Birstall	1	Bramley Road, Birstall	$\frac{3}{4}$
Queensgate Drive, Anstey	$5\frac{1}{2}$	Beechfield Avenue, Birstall	1
The Close, Anstey	$5\frac{1}{4}$	Clark Grove, Birstall	$1\frac{1}{2}$
Beechfield Avenue, Birstall	1	Walker Road, Birstall	$1\frac{1}{2}$
Stonehill Avenue, Birstall	$\frac{1}{2}$	Naseby Road, Leicester	$4\frac{1}{2}$
Linkfield Road, Mountsorrel	4	Lawn Avenue, Birstall	$\frac{1}{2}$
Fieldgate Crescent, Birstall	$1\frac{1}{4}$	Gwendolin Avenue, Birstall	$\frac{1}{2}$
Garland, Rothley	$3\frac{1}{4}$	Farm Close, Birstall	1
Flaxland, Rothley	$3\frac{1}{4}$	Roman Road, Birstall	$1\frac{1}{2}$
Garland, Rothley	$3\frac{1}{4}$	Park Road, Birstall	$1\frac{1}{2}$
Edward Street, Anstey	5	Woodgate Drive, Birstall	1
Welland Street, Leicester	$4\frac{3}{4}$	Ryegate Crescent, Birstall	1
		Middlefield Road, Cossington	$3\frac{1}{2}$
		Harrison Road, Leicester	$4\frac{1}{4}$

(*b*)   What percentage of people in each group live in Birstall?

(*c*)   Which group has the higher percentage of people living in Birstall?

(*d*)   Would you say that the percentage of people from Birstall in each group was:

much the same,
or very different?

> You could answer similar questions to these for people in your maths class.

2 (*a*) What is the mean distance of the Birstall students from Longslade School?

(*b*) What is the median distance of the Birstall students from Longslade School?

3 (*a*) Estimate the mean journey distance of all the students in the two tutor groups.

(*b*) Estimate the median journey distance of all the students in the two tutor groups.

> School buses are available for all Longslade students who do not live in Birstall.
>
> There are 704 students in Longslade School.

4 Estimate the number of Longslade students who use school buses.

> Which students in your school use school buses? How many students are there in your school?

> Some Longslade buses are double-deckers which can seat 76 passengers. Some Longslade buses are coaches which can seat 49 passengers.

C11 page 67

5 (*a*) Estimate the number of school buses required by Longslade School.

(*b*) Do you think your estimate is an underestimate or an overestimate? Explain why.

14 FINDING LENGTHS OF LINES

SQUARE ROOTS

1

(a) 5 cm

(b) 9 cm

(c) 11 cm

Find the area of each of the squares.

2

(a) 16 cm²

(b) 49 cm²

(c) 144 cm²

Find the side length of each of the squares.

I For this square the side length is not a whole number.
What we know is that

10 cm²

side length × side length = 10

The side length is called the **square root of 10**, written √10.
To find it, you use the $\boxed{\sqrt{}}$ button on your calculator.

The side length is √10 = 3.16 cm.

---

3 (a) 24 cm²   (b) 38 cm²   (c) 8 cm²   (d) 150 cm²

Find the side lengths of each of these squares.

LENGTHS OF LINES

1 (a) Copy these lines onto centimetre-squared paper.

(b) Which of these lines is the longest?

(c) List all the lines in order of size.

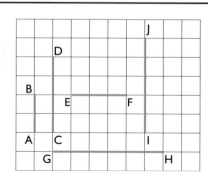

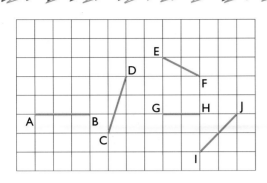

2 (*a*) Copy these lines onto centimetre-squared paper.

(*b*) Which of these lines is the longest?

(*c*) List all the lines in order of size.

(*d*) This question is harder than question 1.
What makes it harder?

PYTHAGORAS' THEOREM

1 Look at these triangles.

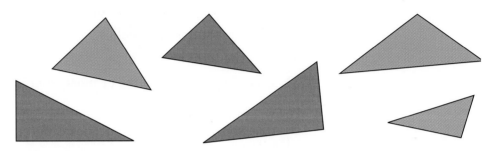

Some triangles are red and some are green.
What rule is used to decide which triangles are red?

2 Here is a red triangle.

(*a*) Why is it red?

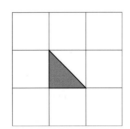

Here is the same triangle, surrounded by squares.

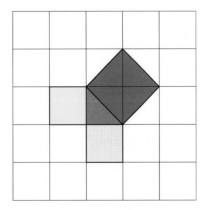

(*b*) What is the area of each yellow square?
What is the area of the blue square?

(*c*) Is there more blue area or more yellow area?

3 Here are some more red triangles.

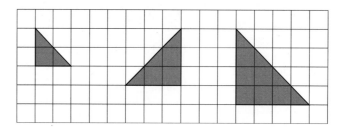

For each triangle:

(a) copy it onto centimetre-squared paper,

(b) surrounded it with squares,

(c) colour the squares yellow or blue,

(d) find the total area of yellow,

(e) find the total area of blue,

(f) find if more area is blue or more area is yellow.

4 Draw several different triangles on centimetre-squared paper. Each triangle should have its three sides different lengths.

Here is a suggestion.

Surround each of your triangles with squares.

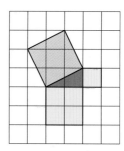

Colour the squares yellow or blue.

Find the total yellow area and the total blue area for each triangle.

What do you discover?

Pythagoras' Theorem

If a right-angled triangle is surrounded by squares, the area of the biggest square is the same as the total area of the other two squares.

In other words, the area of blue is always the same as the total area of yellow.

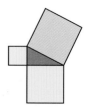

CALCULATING LENGTHS

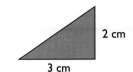

This is a right-angled triangle.

The length of two of its sides are known. This is how you can find its third side.

The length of the third side is $\sqrt{13} = 3.62$ cm.

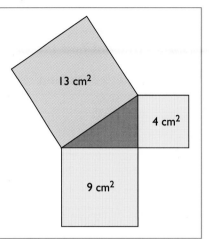

1 Find the lengths of the third side of these triangles.

(a)

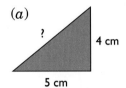

(b)

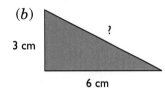

(c)

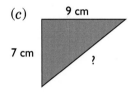

2 Find the lengths of the third side of these triangles.

(a)

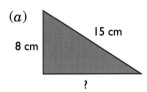

(b)

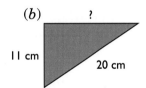

(c)

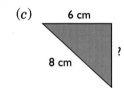

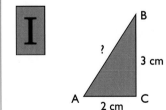

If you want, you can find the length of the third side of the triangle without drawing the squares. This is how.

Length of AB is $\sqrt{2^2 + 3^2} = \sqrt{4 + 9} = \sqrt{13} = 3.61$ cm.

Length of PQ is $\sqrt{6^2 - 4^2} = \sqrt{20} = 4.47$ cm.

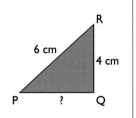

3 Find the missing side lengths for these right-angled triangles.

(a)

(d)

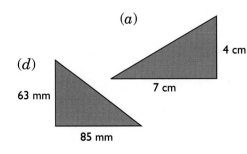

(b)

(e)

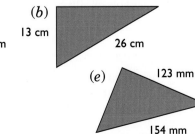

(c) 5.4 cm

(f)

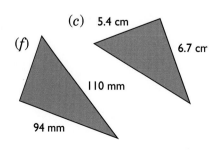

USES OF PYTHAGORAS' THEOREM

 Pythagoras' theorem is useful when you know the coordinates of two points and want to find out how far they are apart.

You can find out the distance between the origin and the point (3,5) like this:

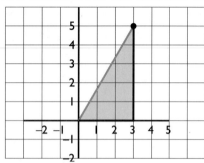

distance is $\sqrt{3^2 + 5^2} = \sqrt{34} = 5.83$

You can find out the distance between the points (2,3) and (6,1) like this:

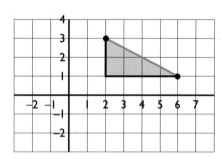

distance is $\sqrt{4^2 + 2^2} = \sqrt{20} = 4.47$

1 (*a*) Find the distance of each of these points from the origin:
A (4,0), B (2,3), C (−3,4) D (1,5), E (0,−6).

(*b*) Which point is nearest to the origin?

(*c*) Which point is furthest from the origin?

2 The vertices of a triangle are at these points: (3,1), (−2,1) and (1,5).

(*a*) Find the lengths of the sides of this triangle.

(*b*) What sort of triangle is it?

3 The vertices of a quadrilateral are at these points:
(1,2), (2,−2), (−2, −1) and (−1,1).

(*a*) Find the lengths of the sides of this quadrilateral.

(*b*) What sort of quadrilateral is it?

 Pythagoras' theorem can be used to solve many different problems where there is a right-angled triangle. Here are two problems of this kind.

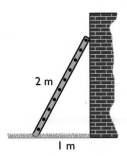

4 A woman walks 5 miles North and then 6 miles East. How far is she from her starting point?

5 A ladder with length 2 m is placed against a wall. The foot of the ladder is 1 m from the wall.
How high up the wall does the ladder reach?

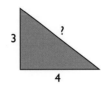

E17
page
110

PYTHAG-OREAN TRIANGLES

1 Find the length of the other side of this right-angled triangle.

3, ?, 4

I This right-angled triangle is special, because all the side lengths are whole numbers.

There are lots of right-angled triangles with whole-number side lengths. They are called *Pythagorean triangles*.

2 Find the missing side lengths of these Pythagorean triangles.

(*a*) 15, 8, ?   (*b*) ?, 7, 25   (*c*) 61, 60, ?

I It is harder to find missing side lengths if you only know one side.

You can use *Spread* to help with this.

Set up *Spread* with 12 rows and 3 columns.

Enter 3 and 4 in columns **A** and **B** on the first row.

Enter the formula SQR (A^2+B^2) in column **C**.

3 Find lengths which will complete these Pythagorean triangles. In some cases there is more than one answer.

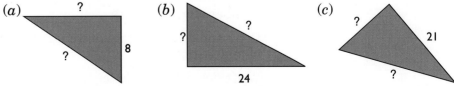

(*a*) ?, 8, ?   (*b*) ?, ?, 24   (*c*) ?, 21, ?

4 Find some more Pythagorean triangles.

15 MATCHSTICK PATTERNS

SQUARES FROM MATCHSTICKS

Four matchsticks are needed to make a square.

How many are needed to make two squares? It depends how the squares are arranged.

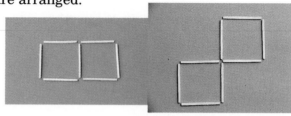

How many matchsticks are needed to make 3 squares? 4 squares? 5 squares? . . .

Is this 5 squares?

STRIPS OF SQUARES

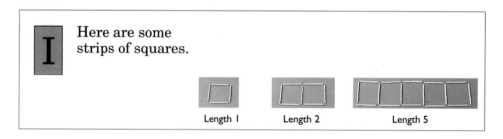

I Here are some strips of squares.

Length 1   Length 2   Length 5

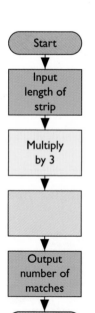

Start

Input length of strip

Multiply by 3

Output number of matches

Stop

1 Write down the number of matchsticks needed to make strips of length 1, 2, 3, 4, . . ., 9, 10.

2 Can 16 matchsticks be used to make a strip of squares?
Can 25 matchsticks be used?
What about 32 matchsticks?
Or 48 matchsticks?
Or 10 matchsticks?
Or 100 matchsticks?
Or 1000 matchsticks?
How do you decide?

3 (a) If you know the length of a strip of squares, explain how to find the number of matchsticks.

Copy and complete this flowchart to show how to find the number of matchsticks.

(b) Write down a formula for the number of matchsticks M in a strip of length L.

4 (*a*) If you know the number of matchsticks in a strip pattern explain how to find the length of the strip. Draw a flowchart.

(*b*) Write down a formula for the length *L* of a strip containing *M* matchsticks.

> This is how you can use *Spread* to find the number of matchsticks needed for a strip.
>
> Choose to have 2 columns.
> Change the name of column A to LENGTH.
> Change the name of column B to NUMBER.
> Enter this formula in the second column
>
> NUMBER=3*LENGTH+1.

5 (*a*) Use *Spread* or a spreadsheet to show the number of matchsticks needed to make a strip of squares of length *L*.

(*b*) Use *Spread* or a spreadsheet to show the length of a strip of squares produced when *M* matchsticks are used.

Double strips of squares

Length 1

Length 2

Length 5

6 Write down the number of matchsticks needed to make double-strips of squares of length 1, 2, 3, 4, . . ., 9, 10.

7 Can 17 matchsticks be used to make a double-strip of squares?
Can 27 matchsticks be used?
What about 32 matchsticks?
Or 45 matchsticks?
Or 10 matchsticks?
Or 100 matchsticks?
Or 1000 matchsticks?
How do you decide?

8 If you know the length of a double-strip explain how to find the number of matchsticks. Draw a flowchart.

9 If you know the number of matchsticks in a double-strip pattern explain how to find the length of the strip. Draw a flowchart.

10 (*a*) Use *Spread* or a spreadsheet to show the number of matchsticks required by a double-strip pattern of squares.

(*b*) Use *Spread* or a spreadsheet to show the length of a double-strip made from a given number of matchsticks.

11 What happens with treble-strip patterns? Or quadruple strip patterns? Or . . . .

12 (*a*) Find a formula for the number of matchsticks *M* in a strip of length *L* which is *W* squares wide.

(*b*) Find a formula for the length *L* of a strip which is *W* squares wide and which is made from *M* matchsticks.

E19
page
111

GRAPH OF STRIPS OF SQUARES

For this activity you need the resource sheet '*Matchstick graphs*'.

F21
page
132

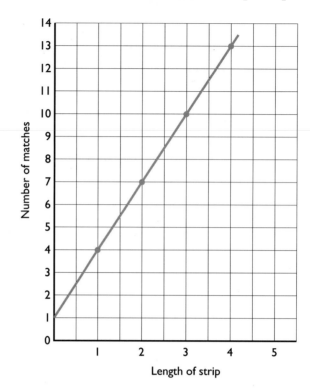

The graph on the resource sheet shows the number of matchsticks needed to make a strip of squares.

Use a graph plotter on a computer or a graphical calculator to draw these graphs. Write about anything you notice.

1 Using the axes for the graph already drawn on the resource sheet, draw a graph for double-strips of squares.

2 Using the same axes draw a graph for treble-strips of squares.

■ 3 Without drawing a graph for quadruple strips of squares, say what the graph will look like.

SQUARE PATTERNS OF SQUARES

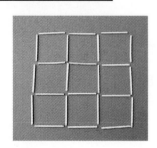

Here is a square pattern of squares. How many matchsticks are needed for it?

One way of counting is to count the rows (red matchsticks), and then the columns (blue matchsticks).

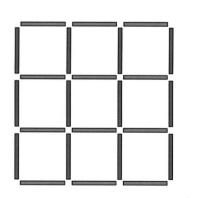

Another way is to count the number of junctions where 4 matchsticks meet, the number where 3 matchsticks meet and the number where 2 matchsticks meet.

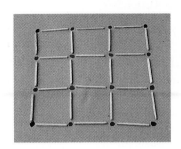

There are four 4-junctions (red dots) $4 \times 4 = 16$
There are eight 3-junctions (blue dots) $8 \times 3 = 24$
There are four 2-junctions (green dots) $4 \times 2 = 8$

This gives an answer   TOTAL   48
which is double what
is should be. Why is this?

Another way of counting is to count the green matchsticks in the picture opposite, and then the purple.

1 (a) How many matchsticks are needed for square patterns of different sizes?

   (b) How many 4-junctions are there on each square pattern? How many 3-junctions? How many 2-junctions?

   (c) How many green matchsticks?

2 (a) How many matchsticks are needed for a 20 by 20 pattern of squares?

   (b) How many 4-junctions? How many 3-junctions? How many 2-junctions?

   (c) How many green matchsticks?

3 (a) Draw a graph to show how many matchsticks are needed for square patterns. The horizontal axis you need is the same as on the resource sheet 'Matchstick graphs'. The vertical axis needs to go up in 4s instead of in 1s.

   (b) How is this graph different from the graphs you drew for the strip patterns?

 4 Use *Spread* or a spreadsheet to show the number of matchsticks required by a square pattern of squares.

You will need to think carefully about what formula to use.

TRIANGLES AND OTHER SHAPES

Isometric dot paper is useful for this activity.

 Here is a strip of triangles.

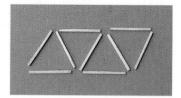

Length 4

1   Write down the number of matchsticks needed to make a strip of triangles of lengths 1, 2, 3, 4, ..., 10.

2   Can 25 matchsticks be used for a strip of triangles? Can 36 matchsticks be used?

3   (a) How many triangles are in a strip made from 17 matchsticks?

    (b) How many triangles are in a strip made from 99 matchsticks?

4   If you know the length of a strip of triangles explain how to find the number of matchsticks. Draw a flowchart.

5   If you know the number of matchsticks in a strip of triangles explain how to find the length of the strip. Draw a flowchart.

6   (a) Write down a formula for the number of matchsticks M in a strip of triangles of length L.

    (b) Write down a formula for the length L of a strip of triangles containing M matchsticks.

   (c) Use *Spread* or a spreadsheet to check your answers to parts (a) and (b).

7   Draw a graph to show the number of matchsticks needed for a strip of triangles.

 Instead of a strip of triangles you can have a double-strip.

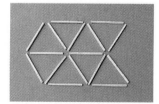

Length 4

8   How many matchsticks are needed to make double-strips of triangles of different lengths?

Triangles can be arranged into bigger triangles.

Size 2

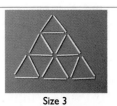

Size 3

9 Find the number of matchsticks required for bigger triangles of different sizes.

10 How many 6-junctions, 5-junctions, 4-junctions, 3-junctions, 2-junctions do triangles of different sizes have?

 Triangles can be arranged into hexagons.

Size I

Size 2

11 Find the number of matchsticks required for hexagons of different sizes.

12 How many 6-junctions, 5-junctions, 4-junctions, 3-junctions, 2-junctions do hexagons of different sizes have?

G27 page 155

13 Explore these ideas for other patterns.

CUBES

1 How many matchsticks do you need to make a cube?

2 How many matchsticks do you need to make a strip of 2 cubes? 3 cubes? . . . Draw a graph.

 Here is a cube of cubes.

3 How many matchsticks do you need to make the cube of cubes shown in the box above?

4 (a) How many matchsticks do you need to make cubes of cubes of different sizes?

(b) Draw a graph. What do you notice about the graph?

REVIEW EXERCISES E

For all the questions in this exercise you will need the resource sheet '*Map of the Midlands and East Anglia*'.

1   Here is a list of bearings from Oxford to several other places.

Town	Bearing
Northampton	075°
London	023°
Birmingham	150°
Bristol	240°
Luton	109°
Reading	330°
Swindon	250°

The bearings have been written down in the wrong order. Copy the list, and put the correct bearing opposite each town.

2   Plan a route from Northampton to Great Yarmouth. Estimate in miles the distance from Northampton to Great Yarmouth by road.

3   (*a*)   Estimate in miles the distance from Cromer to Skegness 'as the crow flies'

   (*b*)   Estimate the distance from Cromer to Skegness by road.

4   Measure the distances and bearings between Sheffield, Derby, Nottingham and Stroke-on-Trent.

   Make an accurate map of the positions of these four towns to the scale of 1:500 000.

1

Oldtown is three miles East and six miles South of Newton.

(*a*)   What is the distance between Oldtown and Newton as the crow flies?

(*b*)   What is the distance between Oldtown and Newton by road?

(*c*)   A new road is built straight from Oldtown to Midtown. What is the shortest distance by road from Oldtown to Newton now?

2   A triangle has vertices at the points (3,4), (7,5) and (5,1).

Find the lengths of the three sides of this triangle.

3   Which of the following triangles are right-angled triangles?

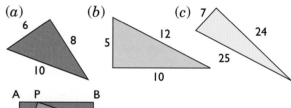

4

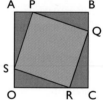

The square ABCD has sides of length 17 cm.

The points P, Q, R, and S are each 5 cm from the nearest corner of the square ABCD.

(*a*)   What is the area of the square ABCD?

(*b*)   What is the length of PQ?

(*c*)   What is the area of the square PQRS?

(*d*)   What percentage of the area of ABCD is green?

5

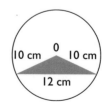

The circle shown has a radius of 10 cm and the length of the chord is 12 cm.

Find the area of the red triangle.

EXERCISE 18 Networks

1

Start

Is the number odd?
Yes / No

Is it prime?
Yes / No

Is it a multiple of 4?
Yes / No

Is it bigger than 20?
Yes / No

Is it bigger than 20?
Yes / No

Is it bigger than 20?
Yes / No

Is it bigger than 20?
Yes / No

A   B   C   D   E   F   G   H

To which letter do each of the following numbers go?

(a) 4   (b) 9   (c) 14   (d) 19

(e) 24   (f) 29   (g) 34   (h) 39

2 This is the route from Clive's house to the post office.

'Come out of the house. Turn left. At the swings turn right. At the end of the road turn left. Go straight on at two cross roads. At the next road by the greengrocer's turn right and immediately left. Then go into the post office which is 50 yards along on the right.'

Describe the route from the post office back to Clive's house.

3 The number of letters in the word five is 4, and so $5 \to 4$.

The drawing shows the start of a network showing this relationship.

(a) Copy this network and add to it the numbers between 5 and 15.

(b) Look at this flowchart.

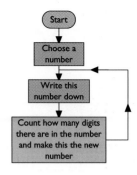

When this chart is obeyed what happens eventually? Does it make any difference which number is chosen?

EXERCISE 19 Equations

1 What number goes in the box to make each of these true?

(a) $5 + \square = 10$ (b) $\square + 13 = 20$

(c) $12 - \square = 3$ (d) $\square - 12 = 3$

(e) $4 \times \square = 24$ (f) $3 \times \square = 30$

(g) $30 + \square = 100$ (h) $100 - \square = 25$

2 Solve these equations.

(a) $x + 7 = 9$ (b) $a - 3 = 5$

(c) $p + 12 = 16$ (d) $16 - w = 9$

(e) $3d = 12$ (f) $5y = 15$

(g) $7p = 56$ (h) $13r = 182$

3 Solve these equations.

(a) $4x + 2 = 10$ (b) $3q - 5 = 13$

(c) $6a - 5 = 4$ (d) $8 - 3z = 7$

(e) $s + 7 = 5$ (f) $13 + p = 10$

4 Solve these equations.

(a) $4x + 3 = 3x + 5$ (b) $y + 7 = 5y - 1$

(c) $6z - 5 = z + 3$ (d) $3 - 2a = 6a - 4$

(e) $8a + 8 = 6a + 4$ (f) $a + 7 = 5a + 14$

5 Sara thinks of a number and tells Sharon. Sara doubles the number and adds five. Sharon multiplies the number by four and takes off 1. They both finish up with the same number.

What number was Sara thinking of?

16 ROLLING BALLS

AN EXPERIMENT

How long does it take for a ball to roll across a table?

'It depends how big the table is.'

'It depends what sort of ball you use.'

'It depends how fast the ball is going to start with.'

Devise an experiment to find out how long it takes a ball to roll different distances across a table.

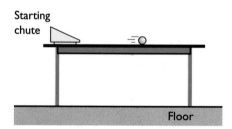

Be accurate!

- Make sure you understand exactly what you are trying to find out.

- Decide what equipment you need and who is going to do what.

Here are some things you need to think about:

- How can you make sure that the ball always starts off at the same speed?

- Are you going to time the ball once or several times for each distance?

- Think carefully about carrying out your experiment. You need to ensure that every reading is carried out under similar conditions. So do not move the equipment once you have set it up. And make sure it does not wobble.

When you have planned your experiment carefully you can carry it out.

Record all your results in a table. Make clear notes about what ball you used – as well as the distances and times.

USING YOUR RESULTS

'How long does it take a ball to roll 80 cm across our table?'

'We measured it five times. Which of our results is the right answer?'

Here are the results a group of students in Truro obtained.

Distance (cm)	Time(s)				
	Trial 1	Trial 2	Trial 3	Trial 4	Trial 5
20	0.38	0.40	0.36	0.40	0.35
30	0.59	0.55	0.64	0.63	0.55
40	0.66	0.77	0.78	0.78	0.77
50	1.09	0.99	1.11	1.06	0.98
60	1.34	1.35	1.27	1.28	1.26
70	1.47	1.50	1.51	1.43	1.36
80	1.69	1.67	1.65	1.68	1.58
90	1.77	2.01	1.77	1.79	1.87
100	2.07	2.05	1.96	2.15	2.05

Look carefully at the line of the table which gives the times for 90 cm.

90	1.77	2.01	1.77	1.79	1.87

The ball was rolled five times. We now need to decide how long the ball really takes to travel 90 cm.

'1.79 s, because this is the middle (median) time.'

'1.842 s, because this is the mean time.'

'2.01 is a 'rogue' value; it is a lot different from the others – someone obviously wasn't concentrating! I think we should ignore it.'

'If you do ignore 'rogue' values you still need to decide which of the other methods to use to get the best value.'

'If you do use the mean time, how accurate should you give the answer? Should you give it as 1.842 s or as 1.84 s?'

'1.77 s, because this time was obtained twice.'

1 Look at the results the Truro students obtained. Discuss what you think the best time is for each of the distances.

B6 page 46

2 Now work out the best time for each of the distances in your experiment.

DRAWING A GRAPH

You could use a computer or graphical calculator to help you draw the graph.

This graph shows the results obtained by the Truro students.

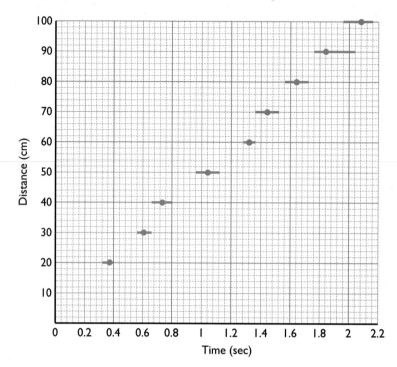

1 What do the line segments on the graph mean? What do the dots mean?

2 Draw a graph for your own results.

I Suppose you want to predict the time the ball would take for other distances. You could join up your dots with a straight line.

'Should the line go through the origin?'

'What's the origin?'

'It's the point where the two axes meet.'

3 Use a ruler to draw a straight line through your dots. (Because the line is straight, you might not be able to make it go through all the dots exactly.)

4 Use your graph to decide for which distance your results were most inaccurate. Check your results for this distance.

5 Use your graph to predict how long it would take your ball to roll

(a) 25 cm   (b) 75 cm   (c) 130 cm   (d) 150 cm

DRAWING CONCLUSIONS

For this activity you need everything you recorded about your experiment, not just the results. You also need your graph.

■ **1** Compare the results for your ball with the results obtained by the Truro students. What do you notice? Which ball was faster, yours or theirs? Why do you think that is?

■ **2** Compare your results with the results of other people in your class. What do you notice? Which ball was faster, yours or theirs? Why do you think that is?

MAKING PREDICTIONS

1 Predict what times you will get for your ball if it starts at a different speed.

2 (*a*) Set up an experiment starting the ball at a different speed.

  (*b*) Time the ball over one distance.

  (*c*) Predict the times for the ball over other distances.

  (*d*) Check your predictions.

F20
page
132

3 (*a*) Predict whether other balls are faster or slower than yours.

  (*b*) Carry out an experiment to check your prediction.

A DIFFERENT EXPERIMENT

How long does it take for a ball to roll down a slope?

'It depends how long the slope is.'

'It depends how much the slope is sloping.'

Devise an experiment to find out how long it takes a ball to roll different distances down the slope.

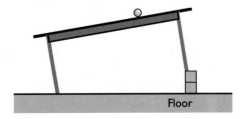

When you have planned your experiment carefully you can carry it out.

115

USING THESE RESULTS

Here are the results a group of students in Fakenham obtained for the second experiment.

Distance down slope (cm)	Time(s)				
	Trial 1	Trial 2	Trial 3	Trial 4	Trial 5
10	1.11	1.07	1.13	1.05	0.85
20	1.27	1.17	1.33	1.20	1.33
30	1.66	1.57	1.65	1.52	1.51
40	1.80	1.74	1.84	1.67	1.94
50	1.91	2.05	1.98	1.94	1.99
60	2.14	2.20	2.11	2.43	2.20
70	2.34	2.30	2.37	2.23	2.45
80	2.74	2.44	2.49	2.52	2.70
90	2.92	2.51	2.89	2.48	2.84
100	2.91	2.79	2.75	2.97	2.97

1 What do you think is the best time for each of the distances in the table above?

2 Now do the same for the times for your experiment.

A GRAPH FOR THE SECOND EXPERIMENT

This graph shows the Fakenham students' results.

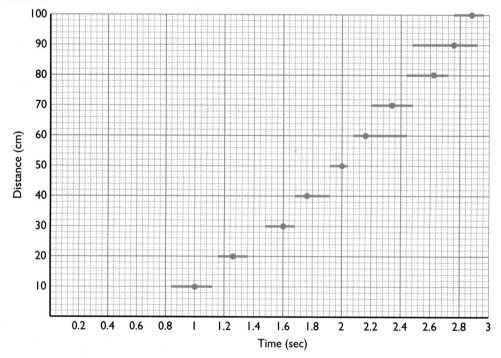

1 Draw a graph of your own results.

I Suppose you want to predict the time the ball would take for other distances. You could join up your dots.

'Should the graph line used to join the points be a straight line or a curve?'

'Should the graph go through the origin?'

'If you use a curve should it be a smooth curve which goes near the points or a wiggly curve which goes through all the points exactly?'

2 Draw a curve through your dots.

3 Use your graph to decide for which distance your results were most inaccurate. Check your results for this distance.

4 Use your graph to predict how long it would take your ball to roll

    (*a*) 25 cm   (*b*) 75 cm   (*c*) 130 cm   (*d*) 150 cm

MORE CONCLUSIONS

■ 1 Compare the results for your ball with the results obtained by the Fakenham students. What do you notice? Which ball was faster, yours or theirs? Why do you think that is?

■ 2 Compare your results with the results of other people in your class. What do you notice? Which ball was faster, yours or theirs? Why do you think that is?

MORE PREDICTIONS

1 Predict what times you will get for your ball if you use a slope which is steeper or less steep.

2 (*a*) Set up an experiment using a different amount of slope.

    (*b*) Time the ball over one distance.

    (*c*) Predict the times for the ball over other distances.

    (*d*) Check your predictions.

3 (*a*) Predict whether other balls are faster or slower than yours.

    (*b*) Carry out an experiment to check your prediction.

F20
page
132

17 RECTANGLES AND HEXAGONS

PERIMETER AND AREA OF A RECTANGLE

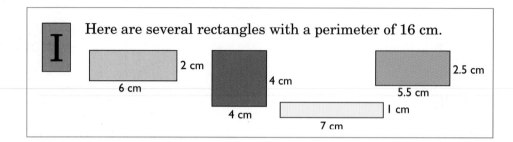

I Here are several rectangles with a perimeter of 16 cm.

6 cm · 2 cm · 4 cm · 4 cm · 7 cm · 1 cm · 5.5 cm · 2.5 cm

1 (a) Find several rectangles with a perimeter of 20 cm.

(b) Find the area of each of these rectangles.

(c) Which of the rectangles has the biggest area?

(d) Which of the rectangles has the smallest area?

2 (a) Choose a different perimeter. Find several rectangles with this perimeter.

(b) Which rectangle has the biggest area?

(c) Which rectangle has the smallest area?

3 A rectangle has a perimeter of 36 cm.

(a) Can it have an area bigger than 100 cm²?

(b) Can it have an area of less than 1 cm²?

(c) Can it have an area of less than 1 mm²?

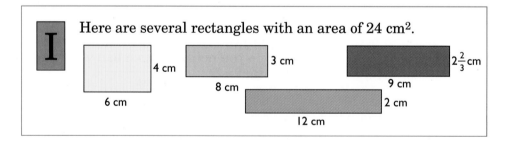

I Here are several rectangles with an area of 24 cm².

6 cm · 4 cm · 8 cm · 3 cm · 12 cm · 2 cm · 9 cm · $2\frac{2}{3}$ cm

4 (a) Find several rectangles with an area of 16 cm².

(b) Find the perimeter of each rectangle.

(c) What is the smallest perimeter?

(d) What is the largest perimeter?

5 (a) Choose a different area. Find several rectangles with this area.

(b) Which rectangle has the biggest perimeter?

(c) Which rectangle has the smallest perimeter?

6 A rectangle has an area of 36 cm².

    (*a*) Can it have a perimeter bigger than 100 cm?

    (*b*) Can it have a perimeter bigger than 1 km?

    (*c*) Can it have a perimeter of less than 1 cm?

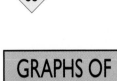

C9
page
66

7 A rectangle has an area of 24 cm².

    (*a*) What is the biggest perimeter it can have?

    (*b*) What is the smallest perimeter it can have?

GRAPHS OF PERIMETER AND AREA

1

2 cm	2 cm	2 cm	2 cm	2 cm	2 cm
1 cm	1.5 cm	2 cm	3.5 cm	4 cm	5 cm

Figure 1

(*a*) What is the same about each of these rectangles?

(*b*) Find the perimeter of each of these rectangles.

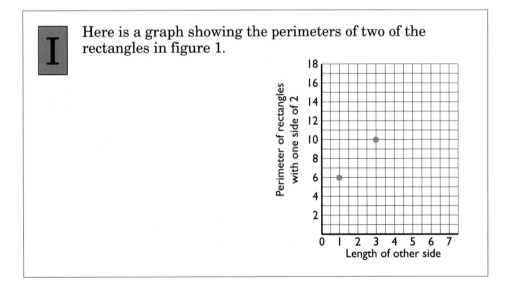

    Here is a graph showing the perimeters of two of the rectangles in figure 1.

2 Copy the graph in the box above onto centimetre grid paper. Put more points on the graph to show the perimeters of the other rectangles in figure 1.

Join the points on your graph with a straight line.

3 What is the perimeter of a rectangle of this type if the length of one of its sides is

    (*a*) 5 cm?   (*b*) 6.5 cm?   (*c*) 20 cm?   (*d*) x cm?

4 Draw several rectangles which have 3 cm for the length of one of their sides.

Draw a graph showing the perimeter of these rectangles, on the same graph you drew for question 2. How are the two graphs different?

119

5 Draw another set of rectangles. What will the graph for the perimeters of this set of rectangles look like?

6 (a) Find the areas of the rectangles in figure 1.

(b) On a new set of axes draw a graph showing the areas of these rectangles.

7 On the same set of axes, draw a graph showing the areas of the rectangles you drew for question 4.

8 On the same set of axes draw a graph showing the areas of the rectangles you drew for question 5.

9 Compare your three area graphs. How are they different?

10 Figure 2 shows a different set of rectangles.

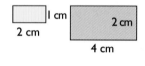
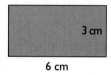
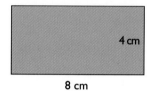
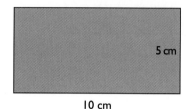

Figure 2

(a) Draw a perimeter graph for this set of rectangles.

(b) Draw an area graph for this set of rectangles.

11 Make up your own different set of rectangles. Draw a perimeter graph and an area graph for your set of rectangles.

Show the graphs to someone else. Get them to describe what set of rectangles you chose.

F21 page 132

RECTANGLES AND HEXAGONS

You will find sometric dot paper helpful for this activity.

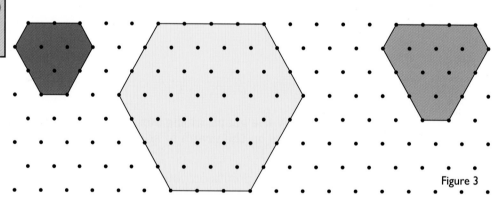

Figure 3

1 The shapes in figure 3 are all hexagons.

In what way are these hexagons like rectangles? In what way are they different from rectangles?

2 Figure 4 shows a hexagon with a perimeter of 18. Three of its sides are of length 4.

Find some more hexagons of this type. Write down their perimeters.

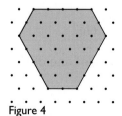

Figure 4

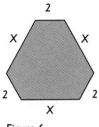

3 This hexagon has an area of 22. Three of its sides are of length 3.

Find some more hexagons of this type. Write down their areas.

4 Look at the hexagons in figure 5.

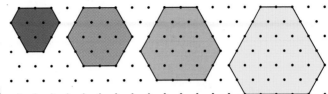

Figure 5

(a) Find the perimeter of each of these hexagons.

(b) Draw a graph showing the perimeter of each of these hexagons.

(c) Find the area of each of these hexagons.

(d) Draw a graph showing the area of each of these hexagons.

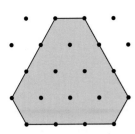

Figure 6

5 (a) What is the perimeter of the hexagon in figure 6?

(b) What is the area of this hexagon?

DIFFERENT TYPES OF HEXAGON

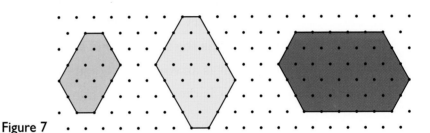

Figure 7

1 (a) Find the perimeter of each of the hexagons in figure 7.

(b) Find the areas of each of the hexagons in figure 7.

2 Find a way of predicting the perimeter of a hexagon of this type if you know the lengths of its sides.

3 Find a way of predicting the area of a hexagon of this type if you know the lengths of its sides.

4 Investigate perimeters and areas of hexagons of the type in figure 8.

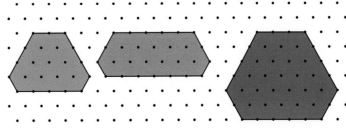

Figure 8

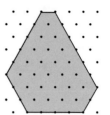

■ **5** Investigate hexagons where none of the sides are the same length (figure 9).

Figure 9

SYMMETRY

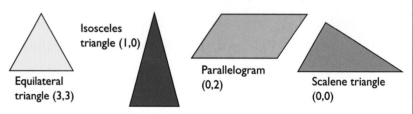

I A plane shape can have two kinds of symmetry. It can have **line symmetry** or **rotational symmetry**.

You can use two numbers to describe the symmetry of a shape. The first number is the number of *lines of symmetry*, the second is the *order* of rotational symmetry.

Equilateral triangle (3,3)

Isosceles triangle (1,0)

Parallelogram (0,2)

Scalene triangle (0,0)

■ **1** A rectangle is an **equiangular** quadrilateral (all its angles are equal).

The symmetry of a rectangle is either (2,2) or (4,4).

(*a*) When is the symmetry of a rectangle (4,4)?

(*b*) What is an *equilateral* (equal sided) quadrilateral called?

(*c*) What is the symmetry of an equilateral quadrilateral?

■ **2** What are the possible symmetries of an equiangular hexagon?

I An equilateral hexagon can be made from geostrips.

Alternatively, *Logo* can be used. There are various different types of equilateral hexagon, depending on which angles are equal. One type can be obtained using this procedure.

```
TO HEXAGON :A
REPEAT 3 [FD 200 RT :A FD 200 RT 120 - :A]
END
```

A film of the different hexagons of this type can be produced as follows:

```
TO FILM
HT
PIC 0
END

TO PIC :A
CS
HEX :A
PIC :A + 2
END
```

■ **3** What are the possible symmetries of an equilateral hexagon?

■ **4** What are the symmetries of an equilateral and an equiangular pentagon?

■ **5** At the beginning of the section (0,0) was suggested to describe a shape with *no* symmetry. Is this the best notation for a shape with no symmetry?

BIGGER SQUARES, TRIANGLES AND HEXAGONS

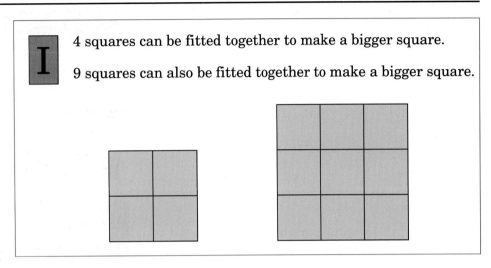

I 4 squares can be fitted together to make a bigger square.

9 squares can also be fitted together to make a bigger square.

1 What other numbers of squares can be fitted together to make a bigger square?

2 Equilateral triangles can be fitted together to make a bigger equilateral triangle.

What numbers of triangles can be used?

You might want to use isometric paper for questions 2, 4 and 5. You might want to use ATM MATs.

3 Suppose you have a lot of identical triangles which are not equilateral. Can they be fitted together to make bigger triangles?

4 Suppose you have a lot of regular hexagons and half-hexagons.

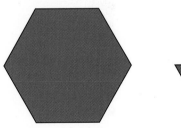

Show how to fit 1 hexagon and 6 half-hexagons together to make a bigger hexagon.

5 What other numbers of hexagons and half-hexagons can be fitted together to make bigger hexagons?

■ **6** What happens if the hexagons are not regular?

F22
page
133

18 HOW THINGS MOVE

THE SHAPE OF THE PATH

Things move in different ways. Sometimes things move in a straight line.

This boat is moving in a straight line. The wake of the boat shows this.

Often someone running a sprint race moves in a straight line.

Someone running a long distance race does not move in a straight line. Why not?

Sometimes things move in circles. Someone riding on a big wheel moves in a circle.

Sometimes things do not move in straight lines or circles. Water going down a plug hole often moves in a spiral.

Which of the following move in straight lines? Which move in circles? Which move in some other way? Describe as precisely as possible how each of the following moves.

1 The tip of the hand on a clock

2 An apple falling off a tree

3 A door knob when the door is opened

4 A snooker ball

5 A ball you throw so that you can catch it yourself

6 A ball you throw so that someone else can catch it

7 A child on a swing

8 The saddle on a bicycle

9 A tyre valve on a bicycle

10 A pedal on a bicycle

11 A goat chained to a post, who stays as far away from the post as possible

12 A person sliding down a helter-skelter

13 A child sliding down a slide

F23
page
133

14 A coin dropped on a moving bus

15 A needle on a record player when playing a record

SNOOKER
BALLS

I This picture shows a snooker table. It has four pockets, one in each corner.

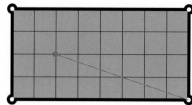

The red line shows the path the red ball takes to the pocket.

This picture shows the same table, but there is a blue ball in the way. The red ball can bounce off the cushion at A and go into the pocket at P.

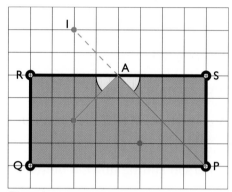

Figure 1

Look at figure 1. To find the path of the red ball you first reflect the red ball in the cushion RS. This is shown by the point I. You then draw a straight line from I to P. Where this line crosses RS is where the ball bounces off the cushion. The ball bounces off the cushion so that the two yellow angles are equal.

1 Draw the snooker table on squared paper.

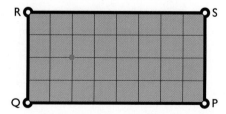

Draw the path taken by the red ball if it bounces off cushion QR and then goes into the pocket at P.

Hint: Use the method explained in the box above. Start by drawing the reflection of the red ball in the line QR.

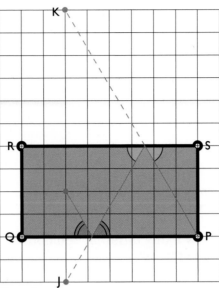

Figure 2

The red ball could get to the pocket P by bouncing off two cushions. J is the reflection of the red ball in PQ. K is the reflection of J in RS.

You have to join K to P first, so that you can find the position of the second bounce.

2 Make a copy of figure 2.

3 The red ball can get to the pocket by bouncing off two cushions in other ways.

Draw the other ways the red ball can get to the pocket by bouncing off two cushions.

For question 3 use 7 mm squared paper and draw an 8 by 4 rectangle in the middle of the page.

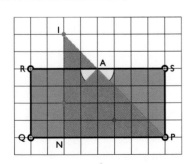

For question 4 you could measure the lengths of the paths. Alternatively, you could calculate the lengths using Pythagoras' theorem.

This picture shows you how to calculate the length of a path. The distance IP is the same as the length of the path shown.

Length of path $= \sqrt{6^2 + 6^2} = 8.49$

4 What is the shortest path to the pocket off two cushions? What is the longest path to the pocket off two cushions?

5 Draw pictures to show how the ball can get to the pocket off three cushions. How many ways are there? Which is the shortest? Which is the longest?

LINKAGES

You need geostrips for this activity.

1 Yellow strips are longer than blue strips. How many different triangles can be made using yellow strips and blue strips?

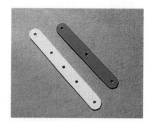

2 How many different squares can be made using yellow strips and blue strips?

3 How many different rhombuses can be made using yellow strips and blue strips?

 Triangles, made from geostrips, are different from squares and rhombuses, because triangles are rigid and squares and rhombuses are not.

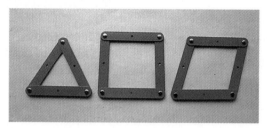

4 (a) Make a square from blue strips.

(b) Add another strip to make the square rigid.

Draw a picture to show where you added the strip.

(c) It is possible to add a strip to a square which does *not* make the square rigid. Draw a picture to show this.

(d) Explain where strips would make a square rigid and where they would not.

5 Use four blue strips and one red strip to make a rigid square.

Now use four red strips and one blue strip to make a rigid square.

Draw pictures to show how the strips are arranged in each case.

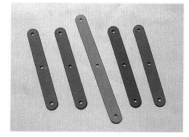

6 (a) Make a rigid rhombus using five identical strips.

Draw a picture to show your rhombus.

(b) One way of using the fifth strip is as a diagonal of the rhombus. What are the angles at the corners of the rhombus in this case?

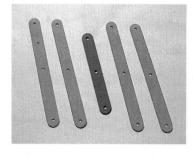

7 (*a*) Make a shape from two yellow and two blue strips.

(*b*) What is the name of the shape you have made?

(*c*) The shape is not rigid. Change the shape. It is always the shape you named in (*b*)?

(*d*) Now connect the same strips together in a different way. Name the shape you get this time. Does it always have this name as you change it?

8 How many different ways are there of connecting up two yellow strips, one blue strip and one red strip?

Do any of the shapes that can be made have special names?

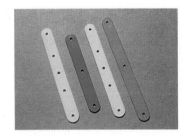

9 Make some pentagons and hexagons from strips. Explore different ways of making them rigid.

■ **10** (*a*) Make a parallelogram from geostrips.

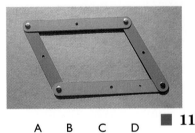

A B C D

(*b*) Keep side AB fixed. Describe how the corners C and D move.

(*c*) Your answer to part (*b*) depends on how the corners are connected up (which strip is on top and which underneath).

Investigate different possibilities.

■ **11**

A B C

(*a*) Connect strips up to make the linkage shown.

(*b*) What can you say about the arrangement of the points A, B and C? Does this relationship change when you move the linkage about?

(*c*) Suppose point A is kept fixed. Suppose point B traces a square. What will point C trace?

What can you say about the sizes of the shapes traced by B and C?

What can you say about the areas of the shapes traced by B and C?

(*d*) Suppose point B is kept fixed. Suppose point A traces a triangle. What will point C trace?

What can you say about the sizes of the shapes traced by A and C?

F22
page
133

129

HOW HIGH IS A FLY?

 A square is fixed vertically. A fly crawls round the edge of the square at a constant speed.

The graph shows how high the fly is at different times.

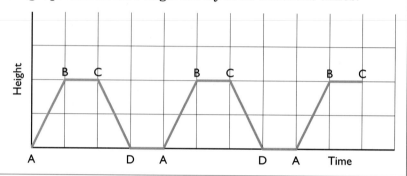

■ **1** Look at the graph in the box above. Explain why some of the lines are horizontal. Explain why some of the lines are sloping.

■ **2** A fly walks round this vertical rectangle.

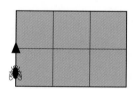

Using squared paper, draw a graph to show how high the fly is at different times.

■ **3** Each of these shapes is fixed vertically. For each shape draw a graph to show how high the fly is at different times.

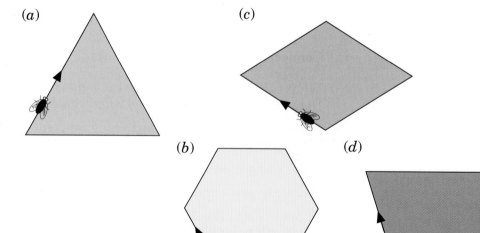

(a)

(c)

(b)

(d)

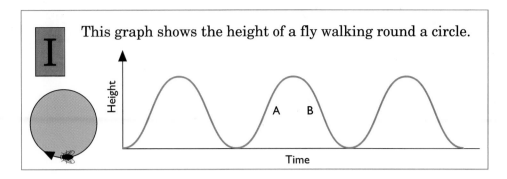

This graph shows the height of a fly walking round a circle.

■ 4 (a) Where is the fly at point A on the graph? Why is the graph steepest at this point?

(b) Where is the fly at point B on the graph? What is happening to the graph at this point? What is happening to the fly?

■ 5 The picture shows a spider and a fly.

(a) The spider crawls twice as fast as the fly. They both go clockwise round the square.

Draw two graphs on the same axes, one showing the height of the fly and the other the height of the spider. Where does the spider catch the fly?

(b) Try different starting positions for the spider. Draw graphs to show what happens.

(c) Draw graphs to show what happens if the spider crawls anticlockwise.

■ 6 Draw graphs to show what happens if the spider goes three times as fast as the fly. Or one and a half times as fast. Or . . . .

■ 7 Draw graphs showing a spider chasing a fly around other shapes.

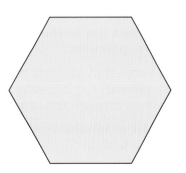

REVIEW EXERCISES F

EXERCISE 20 Statistical Experiments

1 A timer ball is a ball with a built-in stop watch which enables you to time accurately how long it takes to hit the ground.

A timer ball is dropped onto the ground from different heights. The time taken for it to reach the ground is shown in this table.

Height dropped from (cm)	Time taken (sec)
30	0.23
40	0.25
50	0.30
60	0.34
70	0.37
80	0.40
90	0.39
100	0.42
110	0.51
120	0.52
130	0.51
140	0.55
150	0.54
160	0.57
170	0.60
180	0.63
190	0.62
200	0.64

(a) Plot these results on a graph, using 2 cm to represent 0.1 seconds on the horizontal axis and 1 cm to represent 10 cm on the vertical axis.

(b) Which readings would you re-check if you had done the experiment?

(c) Draw a smooth curve that best fits the points you have plotted. Explain why this curve should go through the origin.

(d) Estimate from your graph the time the ball would take to drop (i) 10 cm (ii) 20 cm.

EXERCISE 21 Graphs

1

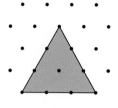

(a) The equilateral triangle shown has sides of length 3. What is its perimeter?

(b) Copy and complete this table to show the perimeters of different equilateral triangles.

Length of side	1	2	3	4	5
Perimeter					

(c) Plot the results of your table as points on a graph. The horizontal axis is to show the length of side, using 1 cm to represent 1 unit. The vertical axis is to show the perimeter, using 1 cm to represent 1 unit.

(d) Join up the points you have plotted with a straight line.

(e) What is the perimeter of a shape with side length 3.5 units?

(f) What is the side length of a shape with perimeter of 13 units?

(g) Explain why the line joining the points goes through the origin.

2 Ann and Sue play a game. Ann says a number and Sue replies with another number. The rule Sue uses is 'double and add two' or, as a formula, $2x + 2$. So if Ann says 3 Sue says 8.

(a) Ann's number is called x and Sue's number is called y. So $y = 2x + 2$. Copy and complete this table showing Ann's and Sue's numbers.

x	1	2	3	4	5
y			8		

(b) Plot the points in your table on a graph. Use 1 centimetre to represent 1 unit of x on the horizontal axis and 1 cm to represent 2 units of y on the vertical axis.

(c) Join the points you have plotted with a straight line. This straight line is called the graph of $y = 2x + 2$.

(d) What does Sue say when Ann says 0? Which point on the graph shows this?

(e) Linda joins in with Ann and Sue. When Ann says a number Linda uses the formula $2x + 4$. So the graph for Linda's numbers is the graph $y = 2x + 4$.

Make a table showing Ann's numbers and Linda's numbers.

(f) Draw the graph $y = 2x + 4$ on the axes you have already used.

(g) What can you say about the graphs $y = 2x + 2$ and $y = 2x + 4$?

(h) Suppose you wanted to draw a third graph which was like these two. Suggest a possible formula for this graph.

EXERCISE 22 Congruence and Similarity

1

Pick out three pairs of congruent shapes. Pick out three pairs of shapes which are similar but not congruent.

2 (a) Draw on squared paper two rectangles which are similar but not congruent.

(b) On your squared paper draw two rhombuses which are similar but not congruent.

(c) On your squared paper draw two trapeziums which are similar but not congruent.

EXERCISE 23 Locus

I If something moves, its path is sometimes called its **locus**. So if something moves so that it is always the same distance from a point, its locus is a circle.

1 Describe in words, or with a sketch, the locus of each of the following:

(a) a golf ball being putted into a hole.

(b) a conker when people play conkers.

(c) a lift in a tall building.

(d) the catch on a window when the window is opened (answer this for different types of window).

(e) the top of a tree when the tree is chopped down.

(f) someone cutting a large rectangular lawn.

(g) a football kicked a long way.

(h) a tennis ball when it is (i) lobbed (ii) smashed.

(i) the foot of a swimmer doing the crawl.

(j) the foot of someone doing a cartwheel.

(k) a dirty mark on a cassette tape when the tape is played.

19 HOW MANY?

COUNTING

1 How many circles are there in the rectangle?

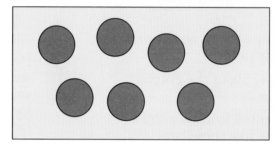

> **I** You can find the answer to question 1 by counting. But it is not always easy to count. Sometimes it might be impossible. So sometimes you have to use other methods.

2 (*a*) How many dots are there in the rectangle on the left?

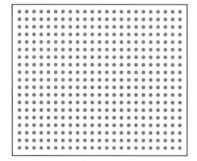

(*b*) Why it is not a good idea to find the answer by counting each dot?

3 (*a*) If every page of this book contained a rectangle of dots as in question 2, what would be the number of dots in the book be?

(*b*) If every page of this book was completely covered with dots like those in the rectangle for question 2, estimate the number of dots there would be in the book.

> **I** It is relatively easy to find the number of dots if they are arranged tidily. It is not so easy if the dots occur at random.

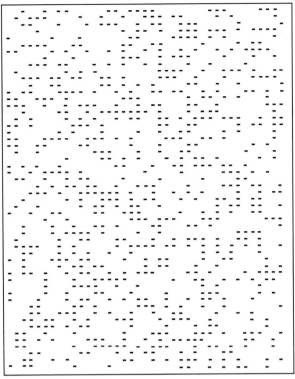

4 This is how you can estimate the number of dots in the rectangle on the resource sheet *'Random dots'*.

(*a*) First cut a square hole 2 cm by 2 cm in a piece of card.

(*b*) Drop the card at random onto the rectangle of dots. Count the number of dots visible through the hole.

(*c*) Do (*b*) several times. Find the mean number of dots visible through the hole.

(*d*) Measure the dimensions of the rectangle.

(*e*) Estimate the total number of dots in the rectangle.

(*f*) Compare your answers with those of other people. How sure are you about your estimate? State how accurate you think your estimate is.

> For question 4 you need the resource sheet *'Random dots'*.

> Use the method of question 4 for questions 5, 6, 7 and 8.

5 How many words are there in this book?

6 How many daisies are there on the school field?

7 How many books are there in the school library?

8 How many bricks are there in a wall?

> For questions 5 to 8 you will need to think carefully about what size 'hole' to use.

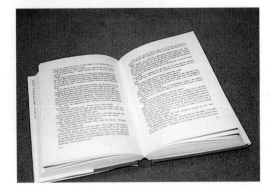

>
>
> The method used in questions 4 to 8 is called **sampling**.
>
> This method is often used to find how many when it is not possible to count.

9 (a) How many people in your class have been to the Tower of London?

(b) Using the results for your class, estimate the number of people in your school who have been to the Tower of London.

>
> The population of the UK is about 57 million.

(c) Estimate the number of people in your town who have been to the Tower of London.

(d) Estimate the number of people in the UK who have been to the Tower of London.

(e) What might make your answers to (c) and (d) unreliable?

10 Use the same method as in question 9 to estimate the number of people in

(i)   your school,

(ii) your town,

(iii) the UK,

who have done other things. Here are some suggestions.

- How many people have ever watched your local team play football?
- How many people have climbed Ben Nevis?
- How many people went swimming last week?
- How many people have been on a beach in the last month?
- How many people like the Beatles?
- How many people went to the cinema last month?
- How many people watch snooker on television?

CI1
page
67

HOW MANY FISH?

How many fish are there in a lake? One way to find out is to use an ingenious sampling method. This experiment explains how it works.

 For this experiment you need to work with a partner.

A Get your partner to put some cubes in a bag. Your partner counts how many cubes are put in (between 40 and 80) but does not tell you.

B Shake the bag and then pull out 10 cubes at random. Mark each of these cubes with a sticky label.

C Put the cubes back in the bag and shake it up again.

D Pull out ten cubes at random. Count how many of the cubes are marked. Use this to estimate the number of cubes in the bag.

Suppose, for example, that four of the ten cubes were marked. This suggests that $\frac{4}{10}$ or 40% of the cubes in the bag are marked. From this you can estimate the number of cubes in the bag.

 The ten cubes are called the **random sample**.

1 (*a*) Carry out the experiment described in the box above. Estimate the number of cubes in the bag.

(*b*) There are several ways of trying to improve your estimate.

One way is to take several samples. You can then work out the mean number of cubes which are marked for all the samples.

Try this way of improving the estimate.

(*c*) Another way of improving the estimate is to take a bigger random sample. You could, for example, pull out 20 cubes instead of 10.

Try this way of improving the estimate.

(*d*) Now find out how many cubes were actually in the bag. Which of your estimates was closest?

2 100 fish are pulled out of a small lake. They are marked and then put back in the lake. A few hours later 100 fish are pulled from the lake and 7 of these fish are marked.

Estimate the number of fish in the lake. How accurate do you think your estimate is?

 G26 page 155

137

TAKING A RISK

 When we decide how dangerous something is and whether or not we want to do it, we often use facts which have been obtained by sampling.

Insurance companies need information about taking risks. The information needs to be as accurate as possible, so that they know how much to charge for insurance. Sometimes they get it wrong and lose lots of money; this happens, for example, if there is an unusually severe storm.

■ **1** In any year the chances of someone dying as a result of a road accident in the UK is about 1 in 8000.

(*a*) How many people will die this year in road accidents in the UK? How many people die in road accidents each day on average?

(*b*) What is the population of the town you live in or near? How many people will die this year in road accidents in your town?

What factors might make your estimate too high or too low?

(*c*) How many people will die before the end of the century in road accidents in your town?

 The population of the UK is about 57 million.

 When you listen to the news, you sometimes hear about millions of pounds being spent on something and billions of pounds being spent on something else. To understand big numbers more clearly it is sometimes helpful to use **standard form**.

The population of Cardiff is 278 900. This, written in standard form, is 2.789×10^5.

■ **2** Write these in standard form.

(*a*) The population of Wales is about 2 780 000.

(*b*) The population of Scotland is about 5 120 000.

(*c*) The population of the UK is about 57 million.

■ **3** (a) The number of people using Heathrow airport in a year is about thirty seven and a half million. Write this number in standard form.

(b) On average, how many people use Heathrow airport in a day?

(c) On average, how many people use Heathrow airport in an hour?

(d) The population of the world is about 5 thousand million. Write this in standard form.

(e) What percentage of the population of the world uses Heathrow airport in a year?

(f) Why is your answer to (e) almost certainly too high?

 The risk of an individual dying in any one year from various causes is shown below:

smoking 10 cigarettes per day	1 in 200
being age 40	1 in 850
accident on the road	1 in 8000
accident at home	1 in 26000
accident on the railway	1 in 500000.

The probability of dying from being age 40 is $\frac{1}{850}$. This is 0.00118. Written in standard form it is 1.18×10^{-3}.

■ **4** (a) Write the probabilities of dying from other causes in standard form.

(b) In any one year how many people in your town will die of each of these causes?

(c) In any one year how many people in the UK will die of each of these causes?

G24
page
154

■ **5** The probabilities of dying from various causes are only averages. Some age groups, for example, are more likely to die from some causes than others.

(a) Which age group is most likely to die from each of the causes?

(b) Which age group is least likely to die from each of the causes?

(c) Which of the causes of death poses the biggest risk to you this year?

THREE-DIGIT FRACTIONS

 The digits 1, 2 and 3 can be used to make several different three-digit fractions. Here are some of them.

$$\frac{1}{23} \qquad \frac{2}{31} \qquad \frac{3}{12} \qquad \frac{21}{3} \qquad \frac{13}{2}$$

One of these fractions is a *whole number*. This is the fraction $\frac{21}{3}$.

$$\frac{21}{3} = 21 \div 3 = 7$$

The three-digit fraction $\frac{12}{3}$ is also a *whole number*.

MAKING WHOLE NUMBERS

1 Use the digits 2, 3 and 4. Use each digit only once. Write down some three-digit fractions. Which of the fractions are whole numbers?

2 Find as many whole numbers as you can by making three-digit fractions with 2, 3 and 4.

3 Now use the digits 3, 4 and 5. Use each digit only once. Find as many whole numbers as you can by making three-digit fractions with 3, 4 and 5.

4 Now try 4, 5 and 6. And 5, 6 and 7 And . . .

IT'S IMPOSSIBLE

1 If you use the digits 2, 3 and 5 you *cannot* form a three-digit fraction which is a whole number. Try to explain why.

2 Find another set of three digits which you *cannot* use to make a three-digit fraction which is a whole number.
And another. And another.

MAKING A HALF

 $\frac{7}{14}$ is a three-digit fraction which is equal to $\frac{1}{2}$.

1 Find some other three-digit fractions with are equal to $\frac{1}{2}$.

Find *all* the three-digit fractions which are equal to $\frac{1}{2}$.
Explain how you know you have found them all.

2 Find all the three-digit fractions which are equal to $\frac{1}{3}$.
And $\frac{1}{4}$. And . . .

THIS MIGHT BE USEFUL

Divisibility Tests

When you divide a whole number by another whole number, the answer is *sometimes* a whole number.

There are various tricks that you can use to find out whether the answer is a whole number.

When you divide an *odd* number by an *even* number the answer is *not* a whole number.

Examples:

63 ÷ 6 and 75 ÷ 8 are *not* whole numbers.

When you divide an *even* number by 2 the answer *is* a whole number.

Example:

68 ÷ 2 is a whole number because 68 is even.

When you divide a number by 5 the answer is a whole number, if the first number ends in 0 or 5.

Examples:

65 ÷ 5 is a whole number.

58 ÷ 5 is not a whole number because 58 does not end in 0 or 5.

When you divide a number by 3 the answer is a whole number, if the digits of the number you divide *add up* to a *multiple* of 3.

Examples:

87 ÷ 3 is a whole number because 8 + 7 = 15 (a multiple of 3).

59 ÷ 3 is not a whole number because 5 + 9 = 14 (not a multiple of 3).

When you divide a number by 9 the answer is a whole number, if the digits of the number you divide *add up* to a *multiple* of 9.

Examples:

72 ÷ 9 is a whole number because 7 + 2 = 9.

67 ÷ 9 is not a whole number because 6 + 7 = 13 (not a multiple of 9).

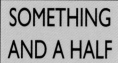

SOMETHING AND A HALF	

1 There is only *one* three-digit fraction which is equal to $1\frac{1}{2}$. What is it?

2 Find all the three-digit fractions which are equal to $2\frac{1}{2}$. Explain how you know that you have found them all.

3 Now do the same for $3\frac{1}{2}$.
And for $4\frac{1}{2}$. And . . .

SMALLEST AND LARGEST	

1 Use the digits 2, 3 and 4. Use each digit only once.

(*a*) Make the *smallest* possible three-digit fraction with 2, 3 and 4.

(*b*) Make the *largest* possible three-digit fraction with 2, 3 and 4.

(*c*) Explain how you know that the fractions you have made are the smallest or the largest possible.

2 Answer question 1, using a different set of three digits.

3 (*a*) What is the *smallest* three-digit fraction you can make, if you are allowed to use *any* three digits?

(*b*) What is the *largest* three-digit fraction you can make, if you are allowed to use *any* three digits?

 In the fraction $\frac{3}{13}$,the digit 3 is repeated (it is used twice). Here are some more three-digit fractions which have one of their digits repeated.

$$\frac{2}{24} \qquad \frac{3}{63} \qquad \frac{44}{8} \qquad \frac{70}{7}$$

REPEATED DIGITS	

1 Is there a fraction with a repeated digit which is equal to $\frac{1}{2}$? Or $\frac{1}{3}$? Or $\frac{1}{4}$? Or . . .

2 What happens if all three digits are the same?

G25 page 154

HOW MANY THREE-DIGIT FRACTIONS ARE THERE?	

 $\frac{3}{41} \qquad \frac{2}{27} \qquad \frac{52}{7}$

are just three of the many three-digit fractions there are. But how many of these fractions are there? It might be helpful to begin with some easier questions.

■ 1   How many different digits are there?

■ 2   How many two-digit numbers are there?

■ 3   How many two-digit fractions are there? Think carefully about whether 0 can be used.

■ 4   How many three-digit fractions are there made from one digit repeated three times?

■ 5   A three-digit fraction can have one digit repeated. For example, it can be made from the digits 3, 3 and 8.

   (a) How many three-digit fractions can be made from the digits 3, 3 and 8?

   (b) How many ways are there of choosing three digits when one is repeated?

   (c) How many three-digit fractions are there which have one digit repeated?

■ 6   A three-digit fraction can have none of its digits repeated. For example, it can be made from the digits 2, 7 and 8.

   (a) How many three-digit fractions can be made from the digits 2, 7 and 8?

   (b) How many ways are there of choosing three different digits?

   (c) How many three-digit fractions are there which have no repeated digit?

■ 7   What is the total number of three-digit fractions?

FOUR-DIGIT FRACTION SUMS

> **I**   This fraction sum is made from four different digits.
>
> $$\frac{1}{2} + \frac{4}{8}$$
>
> This fraction sum is 1.

■ 1   Write down some other fraction sums made from 4 different digits. Which of these fraction sums is 1?

   Find as many fraction sums of this kind as possible which give 1.

■ 2   Choose a different target. You could, for example, choose 2. Find as many fraction sums of this kind as possible which give your target.

G25
page
154

■ 3   Answer questions 1 and 2 again, but use subtraction, multiplication or division instead of addition.

21 WHAT HAPPENS EVENTUALLY?

NUMBER SEQUENCES

I Look at this flowchart. When you use it the first three numbers you write down are 1, 3, and 5. After a long while you get 1239. After a much longer while you get 325 719. Eventually, the numbers get very big.

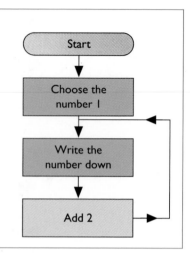

1 Look at flowchart 1.

  (a) Write down the first three numbers.

  (b) What happens eventually?

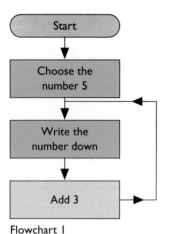

Flowchart 1

2 Look at flowchart 2.

  (a) Write down the first three numbers.

  (b) What happens eventually?

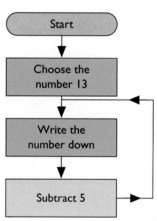

Flowchart 2

3 Look at flowchart 3.

  (a) Write down the first three numbers.

  (b) What happens eventually?

4 Look at flowchart 4.

  (a) Write down the first three numbers. What happens eventually?

  (b) Try using 1 as the starting number. What happens eventually this time?

  (c) Try other starting numbers. Say what happens eventually.

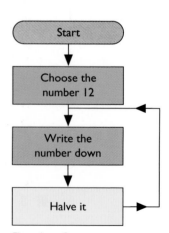

Flowchart 3

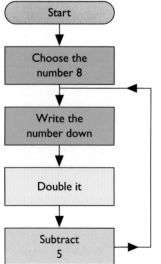

Flowchart 4

Later you will need the answers to questions 5, 6, 7 and 8 for the activity *'Explaining some of the results'*.

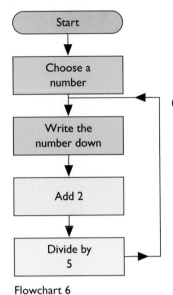

Flowchart 6

Start

Choose a number

Write the number down

Add 2

Divide by the number

Flowchart 7

With *Spread* you can use the formula A = (A+2)/A.

G27
page
155

5 (*a*) Answer question 4 again, but use a different number instead of 5 in the blue box of flowchart 4.

(*b*) Try several different numbers in the blue box. For each of the numbers you try, predict what will happen with different starting numbers.

(*c*) Try different starting numbers with flowchart 5.

For each starting number, say what happens eventually.

6 Look at flowchart 6.

(*a*) Write down the first three numbers you get.

(*b*) What happens eventually?

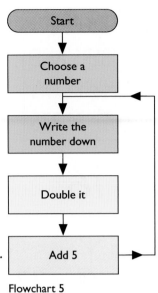

Flowchart 5

You can use *Spread* for questions 6, 7 and 8. For question 6 choose to have 1 row and 1 column and enter this.

A = (A+2)/5

Or you can use a calculator with an ANS button. For question 6, put in a starting number and then type

(ANS + 2) ÷ 5

You can then keep pressing EXE

Or you can use an ordinary calculator.

Enter your starting number, and then keep pressing

+ 2 = ÷ 5 =

7 Use flowchart 6, but choose different numbers instead of 2 and 5 to go in the blue box and the yellow box.

(*a*) For each of your choices, write down the first three numbers, and say what happens eventually.

(*b*) Try to predict what will happen for other choices of numbers in the blue and yellow boxes.

8 Look at flowchart 7.

(*a*) Write down the first three numbers you get.

(*b*) What happens eventually?

(*c*) What happens if you start with −1?

(*d*) Try using a different number instead of 2 in the blue box. What numbers in the blue box produce a *whole* number eventually?

145

HAPPY NUMBERS AND NUMBERS OF OTHER SORTS

16

↓

$1^2 + 6^2 = 37$

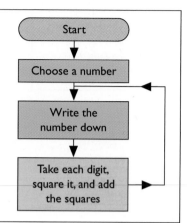

I Look at the flowchart in this box.

If you start with 2 you get these numbers:

2, 4, 16, 37, 58, . . .

If you start with 13 you get these numbers:

13, 10, 1, 1, 1, . . .

13 is called a happy number because you get 1 eventually.

Flowchart: Start → Choose a number → Write the number down → Take each digit, square it, and add the squares (loops back)

1 Try some other numbers.

Which of them are happy? What happens eventually to numbers which are not happy?

I You can use *Spread* to find happy numbers.

First load the file called *Happy*.
Now move the cursor to column F.

What are the numbers in columns C, D and E?

Block enter some different numbers in column F.
Press U (update).

What are the numbers in columns C, D and E now?

Now enter this formula in column F.

F=C^2+D^2+E^2

Block enter some numbers in column F. Keep pressing U.
See what happens eventually.

D13
page
90

2 Use the computer to try other numbers. Which of them are happy? What happens to the others eventually?

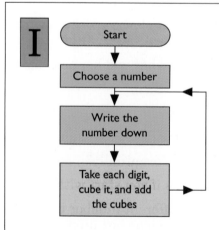

I Flowchart: Start → Choose a number → Write the number down → Take each digit, cube it, and add the cubes (loops back)

The flowchart in this box is slightly different.

Using this flowchart, numbers which give you 1 eventually are called **ecstatic**.

You will find it much easier if you use *Spread* for this flowchart. You can use the file *Happy*, but you need to enter a different formula in column F. You need to use the thousands digit as well as the others.

E18
page
111

You can use *Spread* with the *Happy* file for question 5. You need this formula in column F
F=2*E+D

3 (*a*) Try several numbers. Which of them are ecstatic? What happens eventually to numbers which are not ecstatic?

(*b*) One way of organising your results about ecstatic numbers is to use a network diagram. Here is the start of a diagram.

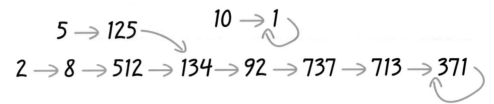

Use a diagram like this for your results about ecstatic numbers.

4 The flowchart for super-ecstatic numbers uses fourth powers instead of cubes.

(*a*) Find what happens eventually when you use the super-ecstatic flowchart with different starting numbers.

(*b*) Use a network diagram to display your results.

5 (*a*) Try different starting numbers in flowchart 8.

(*b*) What happens eventually?

(*c*) Which starting number is not changed when you use flowchart 8?

6 Use flowchart 8, but experiment with different numbers instead of 2 in the purple box.

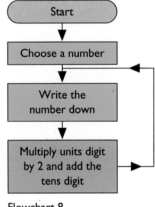

Flowchart 8

7 (*a*) Try different starting numbers with flowchart 9.

(*b*) What happens eventually?

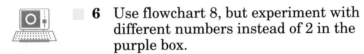

You can use *Spread* with the *Happy* file for questions 6 to 9. You need to modify the formula in column F.

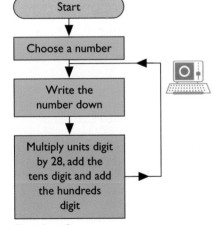

Flowchart 9

8 (*a*) Try different starting numbers with flowchart 10.

(*b*) What happens eventually?

9 Use flowchart 10, but experiment with different numbers instead of 12 and 6 in the purple box.

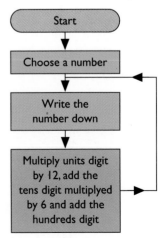

Flowchart 10

EXPLAINING SOME OF THE RESULTS

 In the first two activities many of the rules suggested have *fixed points*.

A **fixed point** is a number which does not change when the rule is used.

Look at question 4 of '*What happens eventually*'? This rule has 5 as a fixed point. The number which is a fixed point is the solution of the equation:

$$x = 2x - 5$$

1 Look at the rules you used for question 5 in '*What happens eventually?*'.

For each of the rules, write down the equation which gives the fixed point. Solve each equation to find the fixed point.

2 Look at the rules you used for question 7 in '*What happens eventually?*'.

For each of the rules, write down the equation which gives the fixed point. Solve each equation to find the fixed point.

3 Write down the equation which gives the fixed point for the rules you used in question 8 of '*What happens eventually?*'.

Equations of this sort usually have two different solutions. Find the two solutions of each of the equations by trial and improvement.

 Look at question 5 of '*Happy numbers and numbers of other sorts*'. This rule has 19 as a fixed point. Here is how you can use an equation to find it.

A number with two digits is a number like this:

$$tu$$

The size of the number is really this:

$$10t + u$$

The rule says double the units digit and add it to the tens digit, to get this:

$$2u + t$$

So the equation which gives the fixed point is this:

$$10t + u = 2u + t$$

This equation can be rewritten to give:

$$9t = u$$

This means that the unit is nine times the tens digit. So the number 19 is a fixed point for this rule.

4 Find the equations for the fixed points of the rules used in questions 6, 7, 8 and 9 of '*Happy numbers and numbers of others sorts*'.

Use the equations to find the fixed points.

THE CHAOS GAME

You need the computer program *Chaos* for this activity.

 For this game you need a dice. You need 6 labels to stick on the faces of the dice. The labels you need are A, A, B, B, C, C.

1 (*a*) Draw an equilateral triangle.

Label the vertices A, B and C.

STAGE 1: Put a dot at A. This is where you are to start.

STAGE 2: Throw the dice. Move half the distance to the point shown on the dice. Mark this point.

Now keep repeating STAGE 2.

(*b*) Can you guess what will happen eventually?

 (*c*) Use the computer program *Chaos* to find out what does happen. Choose three points and choose the ratio 0.5.

 2 Try other ratios instead of 0.5. You could try 0.4, 0.3333, 0.6 and so on.

For each ratio, describe what happens eventually.

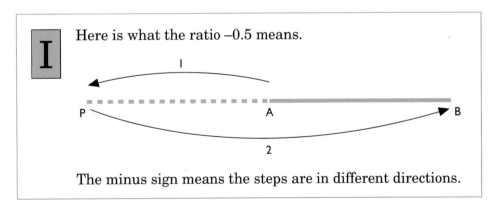

Here is what the ratio –0.5 means.

The minus sign means the steps are in different directions.

 3 Try using the ratio –0.5 on a triangle. Try other negative ratios.

For each ratio, describe what happens eventually.

4 Try using a square instead of a triangle.

What happens eventually for different ratios?

 G26 page 155

 5 Try using a pentagon.

MEAN SEQUENCES

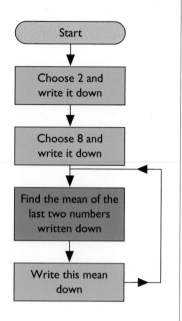

I Look at the flowchart in this box.

The flowchart produces these numbers:

2, 8, 5, 6.5, 5.75, ...

The computer program *Spread* can be used to produce these numbers. Choose to have 1 row and 3 columns. Enter these formulae:

A = B
B = C
C = (A+B)/2

Now enter the number 2 in B and 8 in C.

Flowchart (top):
Start → Choose 2 and write it down → Choose 8 and write it down → Find the mean of the last two numbers written down → Write this mean down (loops back)

1 When the flowchart in the box above is used, what happens eventually?

2 Use different starting numbers in the green boxes in the flowchart instead of 2 and 8. What happens eventually?

Use several different pairs of starting numbers. Try to predict what will happen.

3 Flowchart 11 is slightly different.

When flowchart 11 is used, what happens eventually?

If you use *Spread* for question 3 you will need four columns.

4 Use different starting numbers in the green boxes of flowchart 11 instead of 3, 6 and 9. What happens eventually?

Use several different sets of starting numbers. Try to predict what will happen.

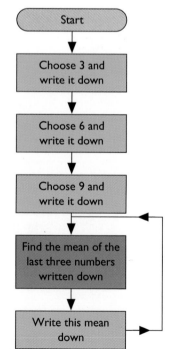

Flowchart 11:
Start → Choose 3 and write it down → Choose 6 and write it down → Choose 9 and write it down → Find the mean of the last three numbers written down → Write this mean down (loops back)

Flowchart 11

CIRCLES

The red circle shown goes through the two blue points.

1 (a) Draw two points on a piece of paper.

(b) Draw three circles through the two points. What do you notice about the centres of all the circles?

(c) Imagine lots more circles through the two points. Imagine the centres of these circles moving further and further away from the two points. What happens eventually?

2 Look at this picture.

Before answering question 2 watch the computer film called *Circle film*.

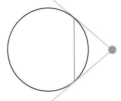

The blue chord of the circle produces the red point.

(a) Suppose the blue chord moves to the right. What happens to the red point eventually?

(b) Suppose the blue chord moves to the left. What happens to the red point eventually?

(c) Say what happens to the blue chord when the red point moves.

RECTANGLES

I The pictures below show squares being cut repeatedly from a rectangle.

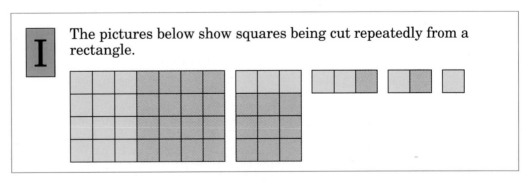

1 Using squared paper, draw a 10 by 4 rectangle. Repeatedly cut squares from it. What happens eventually?

2 Draw a 13 by 5 rectangle. Repeatedly cut squares from it. What happens eventually?

3 Choose rectangles of other sizes. Predict what will happen eventually if squares are repeatedly cut from them.

4 On squared paper draw all the different rectangles which have a longer side of 8 units.

Repeatedly cut squares from each of them. Each rectangle will produce a smallest square.

Draw a graph showing the size of the smallest square, plotted against the length of the shorter side of the rectangle.

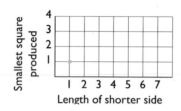

Comment on anything you notice about your graph.

5 Choose a different longer side instead of 8. Answer question 4 for rectangles with this longer side.

Now try other longer sides.

6 One of the rectangles of question 4 has cuts which alternate between horizontal and vertical.

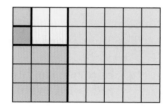

Find other rectangles for which the cuts alternate between horizontal and vertical.

I What happens to a rectangle eventually when you keep cutting squares from it? The answer depends on the *shape* of the rectangle. It does not depend on its *size*. To measure the shape of a rectangle you can divide the longer side by the shorter side.

7 Which of these rectangles are the same shape?

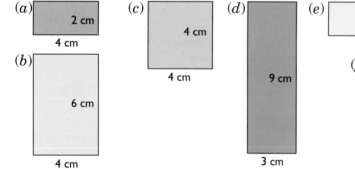

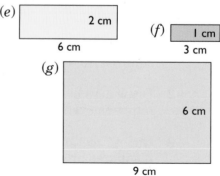

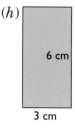

Not all rectangles are like the rectangles you can draw on squared paper. Here is a rectangle of a special shape. it is called a **golden rectangle**.

When you cut a square from a golden rectangle what is left is another rectangle of the same shape – another golden rectangle!

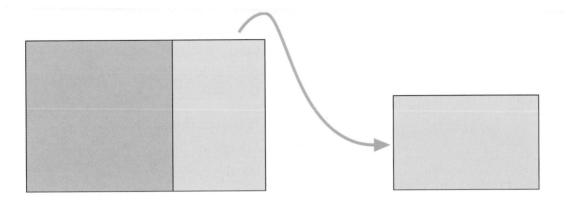

■ **8** If you keep cutting squares from a golden rectangle, what happens eventually?

 Here is a golden rectangle.

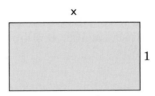

The width of the golden rectangle is 1 unit and the length is x units.

Question 9 is about finding what the number x is.

■ **9** A square is cut from the golden rectangle in the box above.

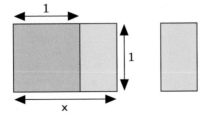

What are the lengths of the sides of the rectangle which is left?

The rectangle left is the same shape as the original rectangle. Explain how this shows that

$$x = \frac{1}{x - 1}$$

 Use *Spread* or a graphical calculator to find x correct to 3 decimal places.

REVIEW EXERCISES G

EXERCISE 24 Standard Form

1 Write each of these numbers in standard form:

(a) 144   (b) 1760   (c) 24.2

(d) 240 000   (e) One and a half million

(f) 0.52   (g) 0.0125   (h) 0.0003

(i) $\frac{1}{8}$ (j) $\frac{1}{80}$

2 Write each of these numbers without using standard form:

(a) 3.23×10^2 (b) 4.5623×10^3

(c) 2.8×10^4 (d) 3.33×10^{-5}

3 List the following numbers in order of size, starting with the smallest:

6.3, 1.28×10^2, 160, 3.4×10, 5.1×10^2, 5000, 1.1×10^6, 2.3×10^{-1}, 9.99×10^{-2}, 0.1, 0.01, 3.4×10^3, 0.0055, 5×10^{-3}, 500, 27.5.

EXERCISE 25 Fractions

1 There are two ways of writing some fractions: for example,

$$\frac{7}{2} = 3\frac{1}{2}$$

Write each of these fractions in the other way;

(a) $\frac{5}{2}$ (b) $\frac{11}{2}$ (c) $\frac{4}{3}$ (d) $\frac{9}{4}$ (e) $\frac{11}{3}$

(f) $4\frac{1}{2}$ (g) $3\frac{1}{3}$ (h) $5\frac{1}{4}$ (i) $4\frac{1}{5}$

2 Arrange these fractions in order of size, starting with the smallest.

$\frac{1}{4}$, $\frac{3}{4}$, $\frac{1}{8}$, $\frac{3}{8}$, $\frac{5}{8}$, $\frac{7}{8}$

3 Arrange these fractions in order of size, starting with the smallest.

$\frac{1}{5}$, $\frac{2}{5}$, $\frac{3}{5}$, $\frac{4}{5}$, $\frac{1}{7}$, $\frac{3}{7}$, $\frac{4}{7}$, $\frac{6}{7}$, $\frac{1}{9}$, $\frac{4}{9}$, $\frac{5}{9}$, $\frac{8}{9}$

4 Work out the following.

(a) $\frac{1}{4} + \frac{3}{4}$ (b) $\frac{1}{8} + \frac{7}{8}$

(c) $\frac{3}{8} + \frac{1}{8}$ (d) $\frac{5}{16} + \frac{3}{16}$

(e) $\frac{1}{3} + \frac{2}{3}$ (f) $\frac{1}{3} + \frac{1}{6}$

(g) $\frac{1}{5} + \frac{3}{10}$

5 Work out the following.

(a) $\frac{1}{2} - \frac{1}{4}$ (b) $\frac{1}{4} - \frac{1}{8}$

(c) $\frac{1}{8} - \frac{1}{16}$ (d) $\frac{1}{2} - \frac{1}{8}$

(e) $\frac{1}{4} - \frac{1}{16}$

6 Work out the following.

(a) $2 \times \frac{1}{3}$ (b) $3 \times \frac{1}{4}$

(c) $4 \times \frac{1}{5}$ (d) $3 \times \frac{2}{7}$

7 Work out the following.

(a) $\frac{1}{2} \times \frac{1}{2}$ (b) $\frac{1}{2} \times \frac{1}{4}$

(c) $\frac{1}{2} \times \frac{1}{8}$ (d) $\frac{1}{2} \times \frac{1}{3}$

(e) $\frac{1}{3} \times \frac{1}{4}$ (f) $\frac{2}{3} \times \frac{1}{4}$

EXERCISE 26 Ratio

1 In a college of further education, the ratio of men to women is 2:3.

(a) There are 1000 students in the college. How many men are there?

(b) In a German class in the college there are 15 students altogether. 10 of them are women. What is the ratio of men to women in the German class?

(c) Is the percentage of women in the German class higher or lower than the percentage of women in the whole college?

2 Rajiv guesses the lengths of a number of objects. The table below shows the guesses and the actual lengths:

Guessed length	Actual length
(A) 10 cm	14 cm
(B) 40cm	53 cm
(C) 3 m	2 m
(D) 10 m	7.8 m
(E) 20 m	25 m

One way of measuring the accuracy of Rajiv's guesses is to use an accuracy ratio. You can work this out by dividing the guess by the actual length.

For example, the accuracy ratio for (A) is $\frac{10}{14} = 0.71$.

(a) Find the accuracy ratio for each of Rajiv's guesses.

(b) Using the accuracy ratio as a measure of accuracy, which of the guesses was most accurate? Which was least accurate?

EXERCISE 27 Number Sequences

1 Look at this sequence of squares:

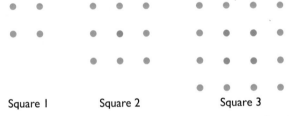

Square 1   Square 2   Square 3

(a) How many red dots are there in each of the first five squares?

(b) How many blue dots are there in each of the first five squares?

(c) How many red dots are there in square 20?

(d) How many red dots are there in square N? Use a diagram to explain why your formula is correct.

(e) How many blue dots are there in square 20?

(f) How many blue dots are there is square N? Use a diagram to explain why your formula is correct.

2 (a) Follow the instructions for each flowchart.

(b) What do you notice about the numbers produced by the two flowcharts?

(c) The instruction in the blue box of flowchart B is changed to the following:

> Treble the number written down

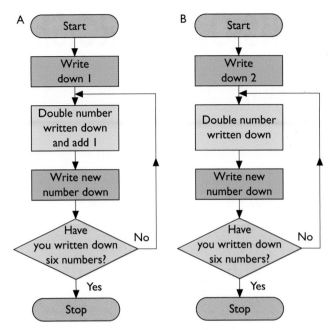

Rewrite flowchart A, so that the numbers from chart A still have the same relationship with the numbers from chart B.

(d) Suggest other changes to flowcharts A and B which keep the relationships between the numbers the same.

3 Here is the start of Pascal's triangle

```
              1
           1     1
        1     2     1
     1     3     3     1
  1     4     6     4     1
```

(a) Copy Pascal's triangle and continue the triangle for three more rows.

(b) Find the sum of the numbers in each of the first eight rows of the triangle.

(c) Predict the sum of the numbers for the next five rows of the triangle.

(d) What is the sum of the numbers in the Nth row of the triangle?

(e) Find the total of all the numbers in the first five rows of the triangle.

(f) What do you think is the total of all numbers in the first 12 rows of the triangle?

(g) What is the total of the numbers in the first N rows of the triangle?

REVISION EXERCISES

REVISION EXERCISE I (Tasks 1–7)

1 Work out the following without a calculator.

   (*a*) 100 – 31   (*b*) 1000 – 317

   (*c*) 160 × 6   (*d*) 162 × 6

   (*e*) 162 × 12   (*f*) 162 × 24

   (*g*) 200 ÷ 18   (*h*) 400 ÷ 16

   (*i*) 464 ÷ 16   (*j*) 928 ÷ 32

2

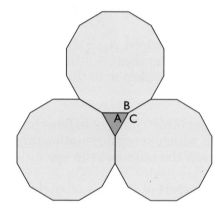

This picture shows three regular dodecagons (12 sides) and an equilateral triangle.

   (*a*) What is the angle at each corner of an equilateral triangle?

   (*b*) What is the sum of the angles A, B and C?

   (*c*) What is the angle at the corner of a regular dodecagon?

3 John used to earn £12 a week for delivering papers. He was given a 25% pay rise. How much does he earn now?

4 A function machine changes the number *N* to the number 5*N* + 4.

   (*a*) What does it do to these numbers?

      (i) 2 (ii) 5 (iii) 10 (iv) 28 (v) 0

   (*b*) What numbers are needed to produce these numbers?

      (i) 9 (ii) 34 (iii) 104 (iv) 1004 (v) 379

5 This picture shows a triangle which is not drawn accurately.

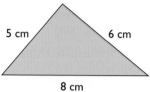

   (*a*) Draw the triangle accurately.

   (*b*) By measuring the height of the triangle, calculate its area.

6 Correct each of these numbers to one decimal place.

   (*a*) 4.33   (*b*) 17.29   (*c*) 0.08

   (*d*) 16.001   (*e*) 27.99   (*f*) 0.954

7 (*a*) How many multiples of 7 are there between 10 and 40?

   (*b*) How many multiples of 14 are there between 10 and 40?

   (*c*) How many multiples of 7 are there between 100 and 400?

   (*d*) How many multiples of 14 are there between 100 and 400?

8 Mary drove 12 miles from home to town in the rush-hour. The journey took her 30 minutes. She returned home in the middle of the day and the journey took her 20 minutes.

   (*a*) What was the average speed of Mary's journey to town?

   (*b*) What was the average speed of Mary's journey home?

   (*c*) What was the average speed of all Mary's travelling?

9 Correct each of these numbers to two significant figures

   (*a*) 4.56   (*b*) 23.8   (*c*) 232

   (*d*) 0.009 87 (*e*) 54 321 (*f*) 0.000 099 6

10 A rectangular board is 1.1 m by 2.3 m.

   (*a*) Find the perimeter of the board in
      (i) metres
      (ii) centimetres.

   (*b*) Find the area of the board in
      (i) square metres
      (ii) square centimetres.

REVISION EXERCISE II (Tasks 8–14)

1 (a) Jason throws a dice. What is the probability that the number he gets is less than 5?

(b) Jason throws two dice. What is the probability that the sum of the two numbers he gets is less than 5?

2 The quadrilateral Q has vertices at (2,3), (1,5), (–1,4) and (–1,3).

(a) The quadrilateral R is obtained by reflecting Q in the *x*-axis. Find the coordinates of the vertices of R.

(b) The quadrilateral S is obtained by reflecting Q in the *y*-axis. Find the coordinates of the vertices of S.

(c) What are the areas of quadrilaterals Q, R and S?

3 (a)

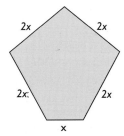

What is the perimeter of this pentagon?

(b)

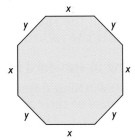

What is the perimeter of this octagon?

(c)

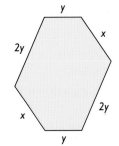

What is the perimeter of this hexagon?

(d)

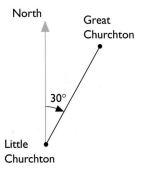

(i) What is the perimeter of this rectangle?

(ii) What is the area of this rectangle?

4 Work out the following:

(a) 4 – 7   (b) 8 – 15

(c) 14 – 8 – 9   (d) (–3) + 7

(e) (–8) + (–5)   (f) (–6) – (–9)

(g) (–13) + 6   (h) (–11) – (–7)

5 Work out the following:

(a) $4 \times (-3)$ (b) $(-6) \times 5$

(c) $(-8) \times (-2)$ (d) $5 \times (-9)$

(e) $(-7)^2$ (f) $5^2 - 2^5$

6 Work out the following:

(a) 6 + (3 + 2)   (b) 8 – (3 + 4)

(c) 11 – (7 – 4)   (d) 12 –(5 – 7)

7 (a) What is the bearing of Great Churchton from Little Churchton?

(b) What is the bearing of Little Churchton from Great Churchton?

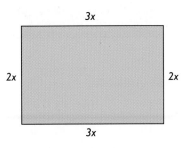

(c) The village of Market Churchton is due East of Little Churchton and due South of Great Churchton. Draw a sketch showing the three villages.

(d) Little Church is 6 miles from Market Churchton and 12 miles from Great Churchton.

Use Pythagoras' theorem to find the distance between Great Churchton and Market Churchton.

REVISION EXERCISE III (Tasks 15–21)

1 Solve these equations:

(a) $x + 8 = 21$ (b) $13 - y = 9$

(c) $5z + 3 = 18$ (d) $30 - 4a = 14$

2

 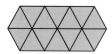

Hexagon 1   Hexagon 2   Hexagon 3

The area of hexagon 1 is 6 triangles.

(a) What is the area of hexagon 2?

(b) What is the area of hexagon 4?

(c) What is the area of hexagon 10?

(d) What is the area of hexagon N?

(e) Which hexagon has an area of 150 triangles?

3 Gareth and Thebender do an experiment to measure their reaction times. Each of them does the experiment 20 times.

Here are Thebender's times, in seconds.

0.26, 0.31, 0.40, 0.26, 0.31, 0.41, 0.27, 0.31, 0.19, 0.28, 0.33, 0.23, 0.30, 0.36, 0.26, 0.31, 0.38, 0.27, 0.32, 0.40

(a) Copy and complete the following table, showing Gareth's and Thebender's times.

Time (secs)	Gareth	Thebender
0–0.15	0	
0.16–0.20	1	
0.21–0.25	6	
0.26–0.30	7	
0.31–0.35	2	
0.36–0.40	2	
0.41–0.45	1	
0.46–0.50	1	

(b) Using one set of axes, draw frequency polygons for Gareth's and Thebender's times.

(c) Which of the two students do you think has the faster reactions?

(d) Gareth's mean time is 0.29 seconds and his median time is 0.28 seconds. Find Thebender's mean and median times.

(e) Do your answers to (d) support the answer you gave to (c)?

4 A rich aunt comes to visit Anna, who is 10, B en who is 8 and Kirsty who is 6. When she leaves she gives their mother £120 to be divided between them.

Their mother thinks it would be fair to divide the money between the children in the same ratio as their ages. How much does each child get?

5 (a) Draw a set of axes. On the horizontal axis mark x from –3 to 3, using 1 cm to represent 1 unit. On the y-axis mark y from –6 to 12 using 1 cm to represent 2 units.

(b) Draw the graph of $y = 2x + 3$ on your axes.

(c) Draw the graph of $y = x + 3$ on your axes.

(d) Draw the graph of $y = -x + 3$ on your axes.

(e) Through which point do all three graphs pass?

6 Work out the following:

(a) $\frac{1}{4} + \frac{1}{4}$ (b) $\frac{1}{8} + \frac{5}{8}$ (c) $\frac{3}{4} - \frac{1}{8}$

(d) $\frac{5}{8} - \frac{1}{4}$ (e) $\frac{3}{4} \times \frac{1}{8}$ (f) $\frac{3}{8} \times \frac{1}{4}$

7 Solve these equations:

(a) $2x + 3 = 3x + 2$ (b) $2p - 5 = p + 7$

(c) $3q + 5 = q + 10$ (d) $8v - 3 = 3v + 8$

8 On squared paper draw two rhombuses which are similar but not congruent.

Calculate the areas of the rhombuses you have drawn. What is the ratio of the areas?

9 Write the following in standard form.

(a) About 872 000 working days are lost each year because of the common cold.

(b) The blue whale weighs about 190 000 kg.

(c) The dwarf pigmy goby fish weighs 0.000 14 ounces.

(d) There are about 500 000 000 tonnes of krill in the sea.

(e) The shortest millipedes in the world measure 0.082 inches.

(f) Apes have been in existence for 40 000 000 years.

(g) The greatest and least circumferences of the Earth are 40 075 km and 40 007 km.

(h) Apart from the Sun, the nearest star is 24 800 000 000 000 miles away.

REVISION EXERCISE IV (Tasks 1–21)

1 Find the volume and surface area of the cuboid shown in the picture.

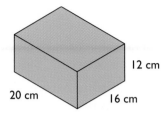

20 cm   12 cm   16 cm

2

> **Facts about poverty**
>
> Every minute of every day, 28 children die as a direct result of poverty in the Third World.
>
> In a world of surplus, three quarters of its population are suffering the effects of poverty, disease, drought and hunger.
>
> One in seven of the world's population is permanently hungry.

These statistics were used to promote a sponsored fast. The population of the world is about 5000 million.

(a) How many people are suffering the effects of poverty, disease, drought and hunger?

(b) How many people are permanently hungry?

(c) How many children die each year as a direct result of poverty in the Third World?

3 The following table shows the proportion of offences of different types recorded by the police in 1991.

Notifiable offences recorded by the police

Theft from the person	0.7%
Theft from shops	5.3%
Burglary, non-dwelling	11.3%
Burglary, dwelling	11.8%
Violent crime	5.0%
Theft from vehicle	17.3%
Theft of taking vehicle	11.0%
Other theft or handling	18.0%
Criminal damage	15.5%
Fraud and forgery	3.3%
Other offences	0.7%

There were 5 276 668 notifiable offences recorded in 1991.

(a) Draw a pie chart to display this information.

(b) How many violent crimes were there in 1991?

(c) Which type of offence was most common? How many offences of this type were recorded in 1991?

4 Draw some triangles which have an area of 10 cm².

Find the perimeter of each triangle.

Which triangle has the biggest perimeter?

Which triangle has the smallest perimeter?

5 Ann has a four-sided spinner, numbered 1, 2, 3, 4. John has a dice.

Ann spins her spinner and John throws his dice.

What is the probability that Ann's number is bigger than John's number?

6 Work out the following:

(a) 3 − 5   (b) 30 − 50

(c) (−4) + 7   (d) (−44) + 78

(e) (−7) + (−9)   (f) (−76) + (−97)

(g) (−5) − (−8)   (h) (−53) − (−38)

7 (a) Copy and complete the table below. You might need to draw some pictures to help you do this.

Number of points on blue line	Number of crossings	Number of crossings ÷ number of points
1	0	
2	1	
3	3	1
4		
5		
6		

(b) What is the entry in the last column when there are 20 points on the blue line?

(c) What is the entry in the last column when there are 99 points on the blue line?

(d) What is the entry in the last column when there are N points on the blue line?

REVISION EXERCISES V (Tasks 1–21)

1 (a) A leisure centre sells cakes at 35p each. If 1300 cakes are sold in a week what were the takings?

(b) Coffee is sold at 45p per cup. The takings for coffee were £148.50. How many cups of coffee were sold?

2 (a) Find the mean, the median and the range of 13, 14 and 9.

(b) Find three numbers which have a mean of 13, median of 14 and a range of 9.

3 The following table shows the average daily circulation figures for National newspapers in 1988.

Express	1 679 438
Mail	1 792 701
Mirror	3 082 215
Telegraph	1 138 673
Guardian	470 023
Independent	375 317
Sun	4 146 644
Today	408 078

(a) Copy the list above, rounding each of the figures to the nearest hundred thousand.

(b) Draw a bar chart to display this information.

(c) What was the total number of newspapers sold each day on average in 1988?

4 A model railway track is laid out as a circle of radius 10 metres. A train takes five minutes to go round the track once.

(a) What is the length of the track?

(b) What is the speed of the train?

5 Arrange these numbers in order of size, starting with the smallest.

$0.5, \frac{1}{3}, 0.15, \frac{2}{3}, 0.23, \frac{3}{5}, 0.35, \frac{7}{8}, 0.78, \frac{1}{4}, 0.14$

6 Solve the following equations:

(a) $x - 7 = 30$ (b) $30 - y = 7$

(c) $3a + 4 = 28$ (d) $3p + 25 = 2p + 52$

(e) $4q - 7 = 2q - 17$ (f) $3(t + 2) = 12$

7 The table below shows the increase in crime between 1990 and 1991.

Notifiable offences recorded by the police

Police force area	1990 figures	1991 figures	% increase
Bedfordshire	53 701	57 032	6.2
Cambridge-shire	44 565	58 167	
Cheshire	55 462	66 297	
Cleveland	73 878		5.7
Cumbria	33 334		35.2
Derbyshire		75 636	25.2
Dorset		51 552	7.6

Copy the table and complete it by calculating the missing figures.

8 A chord of length 8 cm is drawn in a circle centre O of radius 5 cm, as shown in the picture.

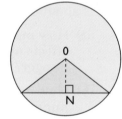

(a) Calculate the area of the circle.

(b) Using Pythagoras' theorem, find the length of the line ON.

(c) Calculate the area coloured pink and the area coloured blue.

9 (a) The lengths of four sides of the L shape are x, x, y and y. What are the lengths of the other two sides?

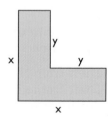

(b) What is the perimeter of the L shape?

(c) Which of these formulae correctly give the area of the L shape? (More than one formula might be correct.)

(A) $2x - 2y$ (B) $x^2 - y^2$
(C) $x^2 + xy$ (D) $x(x - y) + y(x - y)$
(E) $x^2 + y^2$ (F) $2y(x - y) + (x - y)^2$